# Destinations

by the students of
Rutherford County, Tennessee
School System

Wax Family Printing, LLC
Murfreesboro, TN

ISBN 0-9815604-1-5 Paperback

Title: Destinations, multiple authors.
Subject: Literary Collections, Poetry.

**Project Sponsor:**
Rutherford County Tennessee Board of Education
Harry Gill, Jr., Director of Schools

**Project Coordinators:**
Elizabeth Church, Language Arts Instructional Specialist
Jackie Drake, Administrative Assistant

**For Wax Family Printing:**
Publisher: Kevin Wax
Editor: Kevin Wax
Inside Layout: Angel Pardue

Front Cover Artwork: **Destinations**, Kate Troup, Siegel High School, Grade 10
Back Cover Artwork: **Road Trip**, Brittany Lester, Oakland High School, Grade 12
Inside Artwork: **A Day in the Future**, Jayni Kimble, Blackman Elementary School, Grade 4

To publish a book for your school or non-profit organization that complements your
academic goals or values, vision and mission, please contact:

Wax Family Printing, LLC
215 MTCS Drive
Murfreesboro, TN 37129

phone:   615-893-4290
fax:       615-893-4295
www.waxfamilyprinting.com

# Table of Contents

## Chapter Two
### Memories of Friends and Family

# Chapter Three
## Life's Goals

## Chapter Four
Miscellaneous

RUTHERFORD COUNTY BOARD OF EDUCATION

**Harry Gill, Jr., Director of Schools**

2240 Southpark Boulevard
Murfreesboro, Tennessee 37128
Phone (615) 893-5812          Fax (615) 898-7940

February 27, 2009

Dear Reader,

Destinations, the tenth book in a series of student books published by the Rutherford County Board of Education, is a collection of stories, poems, letters, and illustrations that shares poignant examples of life's destinations. Both the artwork and writings are exemplary, providing opportunities for you the reader to experience the joys, sadness, and laughter of each future author and artist.

As you read, I hope you will be reminded of your own life's journeys, reflecting upon the destinations that your choices have provided. Then, look within your heart to discover the memories of your own endeavors.

Best regards,

Harry Gill, Jr.
Director of Schools

**Moving Beyond Excellence**

Chapter One

# Memories of Destinations

## We Spend Our Lives Searching

*Claire Cahoon*
*Siegel Middle School, Grade 7*

We spend our lives searching,
Searching for a destination.
When we find it
We realize that we have not ended our search
But opened another door
To another destination.


## From Mexico to Murfreesboro

*Angel Martinez-Perez*
*Stewartsboro Elementary School, Grade 3*

It all started when I was six years old. We didn't have enough money to buy food or
toys. We were kind of poor. My mom and dad decided to try for a better life in the
United States. They told me where I was going and how our life might be. I was happy
and sad. I got sad because I didn't want to leave my grandmother, but I had to. The
next day was spent packing to go. I was nervous. When we got to the airport, I started
to cry because I missed my grandmother already. When we got in the plane and it
started to move, I started to scream. All the people kept looking at me. I got
embarrassed. It took a week after we landed in the United States to get to
Murfreesboro. I love it here now.


## One Way You Prevail

*Hannah Leyhew*
*Siegel Middle School, Grade 7*

It's where you want to go in life,
Even though it's not a place.
How you get there, I don't know;
Just remember it's not a race.

Some will support you,
With others bringing you down.
No matter what they say,
Don't let your face support a frown.

You should be proud of yourself,
Even if you fail.
Just having a destination
Is one way you prevail.

# The Road

*Chandler Coley*
*Siegel Middle School, Grade 7*

Destination is a place you go,
Whether it's at the beach or in the snow.

You can go to a place that's all your own,
So that you can't be reached by mail or by phone.

Many travel the rocky road,
When their heart is broken and life is cold.

But along the way you'll find the light
To keep you sleeping through the night.

The road to glory is a difficult place,
But when it's done, miracles will have happened at their own special pace.

When you come to a crossroad, you make a choice:
Do you go on being quiet, or do you raise your voice?

Though from the trek you'll veer off track,
Do everything possible to get your life back.

The days on the road will keep rolling by,
Until one day you'll float up to the sky.

You stand before God as He makes His decision;
He studies your life with the utmost precision.

Then, finally, your life is at its end;
It's only then you realize the road is your friend.

## Destinations
*Amy Beth Willis*
*Siegel High School, Grade 12*

Off far in the distance
I see a place of tranquility
Of hope and compassion
Sincerity and love.

A destination of kindness,
Gentleness and everything that is good
No jealousy, greed, or regret,
Only the aspiration of amicability.

The road that we must travel to a place such as this
Requires significant struggle and will never be easy
If we are moving together, hand closed in hand
The way will not seem so long.

Don't dare turn back;
Once near, the alternative seems shoddy:
Hate instead of love, stinginess instead of generosity?
We can never arrive without a collected effort,
So keep on walking, stride after stride.


## My Backyard
*Ethan Boyd*
*Blackman Elementary School, Grade 5*

My favorite place to go is in my backyard.
My yard is not what you think it would be.
If you go deep enough, you can see
That there is a creek, woods, trees, and a good place for camping.
But if you have a good imagination
It is a whole world of magic and adventure.

## Neyland Stadium

*George Michael Huttick*
*Blackman Elementary School, Grade 4*

I remember Neyland Stadium!
I smell buttery popcorn, salty pretzels!
I hear roaring crowds, the rumbling of feet, first down!
I see referees, coaches, many fans, and touchdown passes!
I taste buttery popcorn, salty pretzels, soda, candy, and hot dogs!
I feel thrilled, excited, amazed!
I remember Neyland Stadium!


## The Football Field

*Michael Roper*
*Blackman Elementary School, Grade 4*

I remember the football field!
I smell grass and sweat!
I hear hitting, yelling, and whistles!
I see footballs, scoreboards, helmets, stands!
I touch footballs, pads, helmets, grass, players!
I feel awesome, excited, energetic!
I remember the football field!


## Mexico

*Libby Washam*
*Lascassas Elementary School, Grade 5*

On vacation we flew
To a place where the water is blue.
We saw coral, lizards, and shells on the land,
Colorful fish in the water would eat from my hand.
The band played for us while we dined in the night,
In front of the ocean.
What a beautiful sight!
Outside our hotel there were two pools,
My family and I thought they were cool.
There was an artist there who was very talented.
The picture he gave me was a sunset he painted.
I really enjoyed my trip to Mexico.
I think every family should try to go.

# Florida Memories

*Ashlee Shirley*
*Blackman Elementary School, Grade 5*

Florida has always been
our vacationing spot.
The beaches
are great and the
weather is hot.
I love hanging out
in my swimming suit,
it's much better than
wearing a jacket and boots.
My family and I have
so much fun.
We love being
out in the sun.
I even enjoy the
sand between my toes
and how the wind
off the beach blows.
I'm usually upset
when we have to leave,
but I know Florida will be there next year for me.


# The Beach

*Alyssa Bolton*
*Blackman Elementary School, Grade 3*

Buckets of sand
Eat a picnic
A big ocean to play in
Collect seashells
Have a fun day!

## Going Fishing
*Reece Taylor*
*Lascassas Elementary School, Grade 1*

Last Friday, my famully and I went fishing at Rookbottom Lake. I kot a bass and we kot it for diner. It was good. We went back and I kot some menos. They were brown and white. There were milyins of them. We saw a turtll. He was big and green. We had fun on our trip.


## Come Here, Go There
*Andrew Bluerock*
*Blackman Elementary School, Grade 3*

Denmark
Ethiopia
Swiss Alps
Thailand
Iraq
Niger
Austria
Tanzania
Iran
Oman
Nigeria
Space


## Hawaii
*Emily Yeatts*
*Blackman Elementary School, Grade 5*

I want to go to Hawaii
And see the ocean blue
I want to go to Hawaii
And see a fish or two

I want to hear the dolphins
Make that squeaky sound
I want to go up with the
Waves and then come back down

I want to see the crabs looking
Back at me
That's why I want
To visit the sea.

# Camp Kingsley Pines

*Shelby Jones*
*LaVergne Middle School, Grade 6*

When school let out for the year, it was a bummer;
now I was facing the long and boring summer.
But when I got home, my mom had a surprise;
she told me that I was going to a camp called Kingsley Pines.
I spent the next few weeks getting prepared;
I was very excited, but at the same time scared.
It was a long car trip, but I didn't care,
Because I knew at the end I would **finally** be there.
In the car, I made up games and things to do;
I watched movies on a portable DVD player, too.
I finally got tired, and we stopped for the night,
a few hours away from the campsite.
I spent the night at a hotel, glad to be in a bed,
a place very nice where I could rest my head.
I woke up before dawn's first light
and got in the car; what a sight!
I had never been to Maine, so I just **had** to stare
at all the cool and amazing things there.
There were a lot of lighthouses and antique shops,
and even some snow on mountain tops.
We drove a few hours; I couldn't wait!
A little while later I was at the gate.
I was feeling happy, nervous, and scared,
but I felt better after I saw everything there.
When I met my counselors and my cabin mates,
I knew I was going to have fun at this place.
I said goodbye to my mom, momentarily upset,
but the two weeks were an experience I would **never** forget.
I got to choose what I wanted to do;
I chose art, high ropes, and jewelry making, too.
At my camp, I was having a blast,
doing fun things; I was in paradise at last!
But, my time went by way too fast.
Soon I had to say goodbye to all the friends that I had made;
all of my amazing camp memories will **never** fade.

# Heaven

*Kayla Younce*
*Blackman Elementary School, Grade 4*

Beautiful, gold
Shout, praise, raise hands
I love Jesus in Heaven
Shelter


# Going to Italy

*Chelsey Zhu*
*Blackman Elementary School, Grade 3*

When I grow older, I hope to travel to Italy. I want to travel to Italy because I wish to hear their language. I have not yet seen their life styles. Going to another country is a fascinating and outstanding chance to learn.

I will see what they eat, dress, and play. I will compare Italy to America and see what we have in common. I can learn different, astonishing, and fascinating facts about their history. I will see the different things they celebrate. They may have beliefs and hopes for the dreams of tomorrow.

I will probably stay there for a short time. When I have to leave, I will miss them and they will miss me. My heart will throb with tears of passion. When I leave I will hope to come back soon. I will be sad to leave, but happy to come back to my own country.


# Atlanta, Georgia

*Brooke Weaks*
*Blackman Elementary School, Grade 4*

I remember Atlanta, Georgia!
I smell fresh peaches, funnel cakes!
I hear beeping cars, happy people, laughter!
I see big buildings, the Aquarium, lots of people,
A Coca-Cola museum!
I taste hotdogs, Italian ice, fudge, Coca-Cola from Italy,
Coca-Cola from China!
I remember Atlanta, Georgia!

# Destination

*Luke Herndon*
*Siegel Middle School, Grade 7*

Destination can be an arrival at a vacation, or
Even achieving a lofty goal you've set.
Sometimes it can be the attaining of something long awaited.
To most, arriving at a destination is a great thing.
In other words, you're proud of yourself for completing a goal or journey.
Now on the other end of the spectrum, it can be an
Awful situation, sometimes involving a long anticipated death.
Those can be heart-breaking, but typically,
It is an honorable achievement and a matter
Of getting over that hump.  When you do, it pays off in both the
Near and far away future.


# I Have a Special Place

*Nicholas Emerton*
*Kittrell Elementary School, Grade 7*

I have a special place
Where everything is silent
And where my mind
Becomes as peaceful as twilight

I have a special place and only I can find it
Locked behind a window
That cannot be broken

I cannot share the secret of my hideaway
For now I have written too much
At least… for today.


# The Ocean

*Caitlyn Adolfson*
*David Youree Elementary School, Grade 1*

I want to go to the beach.  It will be so much fun.  I might buy a surfboard and I will be
able to play with it.

## Florida

*Joey Hughes*
*Blackman Elementary School, Grade 4*

I remember Florida!
I smell the ocean, churos!
I hear water splashing, boats, trees rustling!
I see a jumping mullet, sneaky alligators, resting sea stars,
Fast lizards!
I touch freshly, cut grass, dancing water,
Soft sand, smooth leather,
Jumbo-sized leaves!
I feel scared, excited, wonderful!
I remember Florida!


## This Is My Year

*Joanna Nyland*
*Smyrna High School, Grade 11*

Last year, I was a surprise to the swim team, an oddity, someone who just came out of nowhere. The first time I competed in a meet, I surprised everyone. I didn't come in first, but I gave the other team's competitor a run for her money. I progressively got better last year, swimming faster and faster times at almost every meet. At the county meet, I placed third, an almost unimaginable accomplishment for someone who had never swum seriously before. I qualified for the regional meet early in the season, but I was aiming higher. I wanted to compete in the state swim meet. I swam my best time at the regional meet, but I didn't qualify for state. I felt as if I had let my coach down, my team down, and I let myself down.

Last year, I competed at state on a relay. I swam my hardest, pushing my body past its limits, but it wasn't outstanding. I watched the rest of my team from the bleachers, cheering for the people who had become my family over the past five months of getting up at the crack of dawn every weekday morning that we had school, of spending over two hours in the pool during Christmas break every day except for Christmas Day, New Year's Day, and weekends. I was happy for them, but I wished I could compete with them in an individual event.

This year, my destination is the Tennessee State Swimming Championship. I will qualify, I will swim the 100-meter breaststroke, and I will succeed. Last year I was less than a second away from swimming one of the biggest races of my life; this year I will reach my destination.

# Logan's Judgment

*Grace Pogue*
*Oakland High School, Grade 9*

Logan Chambers was a modern-day god. He exhibited prodigious qualities of perfection that radiated from his extremely tanned body to the people around him. Just being in the same proximity to him seemed unreal, on the verge of ethereal. Not only was he Abercrombie model material, his attitude and personality created a delusion of serenity and lightheartedness. For many unsuspecting high school girls, they would soon fall under his spell, whether that was his deliberate plan or not. He would become their entire world, and girls would give their most prized possession just to be his. Every girl became instantly angelic in his presence, but behind his beautiful, hazel eyes, it was a war zone. And on this certain day, it all started with one piece of paper.

The dawn of World War III came to exist on the first Monday of April. Prom season. Every junior and senior girl's dream, or otherwise nightmare. The day began with the usual Monday morning Algebra II class, with three normal high school girls, but only one shared desire. In one corner, the ignoble Rebecca Donaldson was apparently not paying any attention to Mr. Campbell's lecture on multiplicative inverses and was absent-mindedly doodling "Mrs. Rebecca Chambers" on her math notebook. Directly two rows back, Megan Whittaker was semi-paying attention to the lecture, but had more focus on stretching her Achilles tendon for tonight's big game against Riverside. On the other side of the room, Lauran Giovanni was aimlessly trying to reapply her mascara without the use of a mirror, and therefore leaving heavy black blotches on the upper half of her eyelid. Putting the mascara back into her vintage Louis Vuitton handbag, she turned her attention to a much more interesting subject: a gorgeous boy who happened to be sitting precisely in the center of the room, pen in hand, notebook open.

Riiiiinnnnngggg! The bell was more of an actual wake-up call than a reminder to leave class. As soon as the class was dismissed, Logan Chambers raced out of the classroom as not to be late to his related arts class. On his exit, he accidently dropped a single, carefully folded piece of regular notebook paper, and of course, caught the attention of three girls who did not feel the need to rush to their second period class. The first to grab it however, was Megan Whittaker, who obviously had more agility and speed than the other two girls.

"What do you think you are doing?" Rebecca snarled as Megan began to open the note.

"Yeah, you have no right to read that!" Lauran suddenly chimed in, who came in from behind-the-scenes.

"Oh, cut it out, both of you! You both know you are dying to read it as much as I am! Now be quiet so I can read this aloud!" Megan stated with no hesitation.

But there was no reason to read anything aloud. Less than ten words appeared on the page. On the page, written in Logan's perfectly slanted handwriting, was the simple question, "Will you go to the dance with me?"

Before Megan could look up from the paper in her hands, Rebecca and Lauran did everything but fly out the door to chase after their beloved Logan.

"Oh, Logan!" Rebecca called nearly two yards away from him in the hallway. She got to him first, Lauran walking laggardly to her next class.

"Oh, um, hey, Rebecca. What's up?" Logan asked, flashing his million dollar smile.

"Oh, nothing. I was just wondering if you have given any thought to prom. I don't mean to obtrude, but you know it's only a few weeks away. I just want to make sure you don't feel left out or anything. And of course that you have a good time! Speaking of a good time, I know someone who would be *perfect* for you to go with!"

"Oh, really? And who might that be?" Logan sincerely questioned.

"Oh, silly boy! Me, of course! Oh my gosh, it will be so much fun! Just think about it, okay?"

"Will do, Rebecca. Well, I've got to run, don't want to be late. See you around," he said as he waved.

"Easy as pie," Rebecca thought as she made her way to her next class.

*   *   *

Second period seemed to go by extremely slowly for Lauran as she personally counted down the clock until the bell rang. And when it did, she jumped from her seat and ran across the room to find her believed soul mate.

"Hey, Logan!" Lauran seemed to shout from all the way from across the courtyard. Bystanders looked up from their efforts to do last-minute homework.

"We need to talk!"

"Hey, Lauran. What is this I hear we need to talk about?" Logan kindly acknowledged the fact he learned this from hearing it 50 yards away.

"Prom, duh! We *totally* need to go together! It'll be oober fun! So much fun to have, so little time to plan! What do you say, pick you up at 7:35ish?"

"Oh um, prom, right. Well I don't know about all that yet. I haven't really given it that much thought. I will let you know A.S.A.P. though," Logan said kindly.

"All right! Most definitely! Well, catch you on the flip-side! Bye!" Lauran almost screamed as she skipped away, thrilled.

*   *   *

Megan watched the clock in world history as she did every day for the past eight months. Her stomach growled.

"Yes, lunch!" she thought as she hoped for a substantive amount of food. She would need all the strength and energy she could manage for the biggest game of her life tonight. The bell suddenly rang, and she jolted out of there as fast as her athletically-built legs could take her. The lunch room was as crowded as she feared. She grabbed a tray and sat against the wall as the line to the food slowly moved forward. While waiting, Logan walked into the cafeteria. Cue the doves, Hallelujah chorus, and rays of sunshine. Yet she was used to this kind of reaction he gave her. She only has had a crush on him since the second grade. She barely even thought he knew that she existed. But that was all about to change.

"Hey, Megan!" Logan bellowed from his deep voice. He was standing right next to her with a tray in his hand.

"Oh, hey, Logan." Had her heart stopped beating? She could not tell.

"Hey, so um, good luck in the big game tonight against Riverside. I'll be there cheering for you. I bet you'll do awesome," Logan smiled as he complimented her.

Megan blushed, "Oh, thanks. I'm extremely nervous. I probably won't even be able to keep this food down."

"I think that's just how the cafeteria food reacts to the stomach," Logan joked.

"Oh, yeah. You're probably right." "Like usual," she thought.

"Well actually, I kinda wanted to mention something else to you if you don't

14

mind. Well, you see, prom is coming up, and I was wondering if you'd like to go. Ya know, with me."

Megan stared at him blankly.

"Well, it's okay if you don't want to, I was just giving you the option," Logan said, embarrassed.

"Oh, Logan, I'd love to go with you!" Megan yelped, a dream come true.

"Okay, great! Pick you up at 8 then!" Logan said, ecstatically.

"Great, it's a date." Megan winked as he turned to sit down with his baseball buddies.

Megan could not believe her luck! She had only dreamed about this since she hit puberty. Everything was momentarily perfect, until one thought cringed upon her mind. What was she going to wear?


## The Football Field
*Matthew Sells*
*Blackman Elementary School, Grade 4*

I remember the football field!
I smell wet grass, sweat!
I hear hitting,
cracking, touchdown!
I see people hitting, yelling coaches, a long field,
the brown football!
I touch the rough ball, wet field,
End zone, hard helmets,
Players!
I feel great, fantastic, excited!
I remember the football field!

# Freedom

*Mandy Godwin*
*Oakland High School, Grade 9*

The sky is perfect today. A slight breeze from the harbor ruffles my hair as I hang my feet over the dock. All around, men are rushing to and fro, busy with the new demand for ships. Many of them, especially the younger ones like me, radiate excitement. None of us have seen real war before, but we are more than eager to stand as one, to protect what we believe in. I would never say so to my father, but I have hope for this new country, too.

Quietly, I slip off my shoes and stockings, and dip my feet into the cool water. I am thankful the dock supervisor is too exasperated to notice me these days, for he has reprimanded me many times for removing my shoes. He does not feel it is appropriate for a young man to splash around like a child. We do not see eye to eye. While I am not as enamored by the sea as my older brother Thomas, there is a comfort in it. The way the Boston Harbor touches the horizon, blurring the line between the heavens and the ocean, puts a part of me at peace, knowing that all is connected. Footsteps from behind startle me from my stupor.

"Hello John, how fare you?" A strong hand claps my shoulder, and I look up, meeting the grim gaze of my oldest brother William.

"I am well," I respond slowly, troubled by the darkness in his eyes. He sighs, looking away.

"Father did not tell you, then." It is not a question. I stare up at my brother, a sinking feeling in my gut. He glances back at me, pity shadowing his expression. "He is taking the family back to England."

A fire washes over me. I say nothing, but close my eyes and try to fight off the simmering anger. In frustration, I slam a fist against the wood.

"John."

William's voice is displeased. I am nearly eighteen, I am to act a gentleman. He tries to change the subject. "What are you still doing here? You are free to go at three, are you not? It is nearly five."

"I did not want to leave." I grab my stockings, pulling them on quickly, not caring how sodden they will be. William shoots me a withering look.

"Don't be selfish, John. Mother and the girls need your help at home."

I do not respond. There is nothing I can say that will not result in an argument. I stand, and giving my brother a curt nod, trot towards home. I can feel his eyes on me. He is father's golden boy, and neither of them understand me.

Mother, sitting in the parlor with needle and thread, greets me softly when I arrive. Not a moment after I remove my hat, my three little sisters come rushing towards me. Mary, at five the youngest, wraps her arms around me. Despite my sour mood, I cannot help but laugh. Anna and Bethany giggle. I open my arms wide enough for all three of them, and their levity makes me chuckle, too. The sound of my father's voice shoots ice through my veins.

"John," he says, appearing at the doorway of his study, "come here."

My sisters shy away from me, their eyes down. I stride silently into the room. Father sits at his desk, and I take the leather seat across from him. I shift uncomfortably, remembering the times throughout my childhood Father gave me a stern scolding here. It teems with books and impressive looking documents, but the pungent odor of dust nearly makes me sneeze. Father's gaze is cold, uncaring. He is going to tell me we are leaving, then be done with me. He never cared for my assent.

"Where did you get that?" he demands, glaring at the tri-corn in my hand. His question startles me.

"Fr-from Peter. He works at the shipyard with me sometimes, sir." I hate the stutter in my voice. Unconsciously, I draw the hat closer. All the money I earn goes to my family, so I'd taken over Peter's responsibilities for three weeks to get this. Father snatches it from my hands.

"This! This is a rebel's hat. Those dogs that think they can break away from the motherland, this is what they wear!" He shoves it in my face, then throws it down, grinding it with the toe of his boot.

"No," I breathe. It was meant in stunned disbelief, not defiance, but Father takes it the wrong way. His face becomes bright red, and he turns on me.

"The next ship for England departs tomorrow morning. This family is going to be on it. I will not let my son be swayed by the foolish notions of an uprising! Get your things together, boy."

He is sneering at me as I turn and flee.

*\*\**

Thunder and lightning greet me the next morning, accompanied by a light, steady drizzle. My things are scattered haphazardly across the room. I am sure my face looks gaunt and haggard, but I have reached my decision. There is no turning back now.

Someone is calling my name. I'd thought no one else was awake. Reluctantly, I slink downstairs. I find myself standing face to face with my mother. It is in her eyes, some ethereal force that tells me she knows. Suddenly, my petite, submissive mother takes me in her arms and hugs me fiercely.

"I'm proud of you, John," she whispers. After a moment she pulls away, tears in her eyes. I smile.

"Don't worry, Mother. I'll be alright." She smiles back at me.

"I know."

My heart light, I walk through the door. The rain has slowed, and the scent of the harbor has mixed with the fresh smell of the earth. It is my heaven, my freedom. Determination pounds though me, matching the rhythm of my feet against the cobblestone. I have won the battle against my own oppression; now I fight for a more important liberty. I don dmy battered tri-corn, and daybreak finally greets me.

## McDonald's

*Donovan Sims*
*Blackman Elementary School, Grade 4*

I remember McDonald's!
I smell fries, chicken nuggets!
I hear talking,
sizzling fries, drinks filling up!
I see chicken nuggets, fries, chicken sandwiches,
cheeseburgers!
I taste salt, potatoes, Sprite, chicken nuggets,
And chicken sandwiches!
I feel great, amazing, satisfied!
I remember McDonald's!


## Destinations

*Clint Judkins*
*Lascassas Elementary School, Grade 6*

I have learned that destinations are not just places we go to in the car. Destinations are also places we go to in our minds. It can be memories, hopes, and dreams. Memories of family vacations are my favorite. There are many to choose from, but the best for me is remembering all the fun I have had in Gatlinburg, Tennessee.

I have been to Gatlinburg many times with my mom and dad. We always stay at the same hotel way up in the mountains. The hotel has fifteen floors with big lights that hang all the way down. The pool is always warm and has a waterfall! This is where I learned to swim. I loved when my dad got in too and put me on his shoulders then tossed me into the water.

Every visit included riding with my dad in go-carts until at last I was ready to drive on my own. I was overjoyed to be behind the wheel and racing my dad. The speed, the noise of the go-cart, and the laughs of everyone having a great time was a thrill I'll never forget. After a lot of races on many different tracts, my mom told me that dad was as proud as I was excited to finally beat him on the track!

There are a lot of other memories about these trips that make me smile. One is knowing no matter how many times we visit, we will make time to go to Pigeon Forge to this little souvenir store that has live bears. The bears are kept in a little zoo out back. We buy apples and bread to feed the bears. There are stairs that visitors climb to put them up over the bears' den to toss the food down to them. If you toss the apple slices just right, the bears will catch it in their mouths.

No matter what we do when we go on this trip, I really just love the good feeling I get when we go and thinking about it when we get home. I get to go again in my mind by telling people about the things we did, showing my souvenirs, and looking through the pictures. There have been other great vacations in different cities, but none that I like to go to in my mind as much.

## Nothing but a Dream

*Samantha Holloran*
*Rock Springs Middle School, Grade 6*

As tears rolled down my face I gave a smile from my dry lips. I was heading towards a place where death was no problem. This destination is a magical place where you would no longer worry about dying until old age arrives. It might sound a bit overwhelming, but it is a place where I hoped I was going. My eyes opened to my bedroom light in my eyes. I looked around, I knew that I wasn't in my destination's zone, and the magical place was gone. My joyous smile turned into a frown of deep sorrow. My destination turned into a dream in the blink of an eye. I have never seen that place since then, but I have confidence that it will come to me again some day. I guess I discovered that reality isn't a dream and my dream wasn't even close to reality.


## My Destinations

*Lesley Hillis*
*Christiana Elementary School, Grade 5*

My destination is Hawaii
Oh, I hope I can go there!
I'd love to see the scenery,
And ride the ocean blue.
I hope to see some dolphins,
And maybe a squid or two.
Some jellyfish would be cool,
Or maybe some sharks.
Oh, how I would like to go to Hawaii!

## What a Trip!

*John-Michael Green*
*Christiana Elementary School, Grade 5*

I was seven when we went to New York. My family had to get up at four o'clock in the morning. After we woke up, we got everything packed into the car and ate breakfast. Then, we were on our way to New York. First we had to go to my grandparent's house. We met my grandma there, and she brought us to the store to get gum for the plane. She dropped us off at the airport, and we had to wait in line forever to get on the plane.

We finally got on the plane with all of our stuff. The plane took us to another airport. Then, we got on another plane that went to New York City. When we arrived, my other grandmother and cousin picked us up and took us to their house. When we arrived at their house, we met my uncle and his son. We also went out to eat that day. The food was so good.

When we got back to my uncle's house, my godfather and godmother pulled in the driveway. They gave me my first Playstation. After that, they gave me a game. At only seven years old, I was thrilled to have my first Playstation and a game. Next, my cousin asked me to go to the skating rink. I said, "YES!!" Then I found out that my cousin worked there. "Awesome!" I exclaimed. After the skating rink, we went back to their house. My dad took me to the store in my cousin's Mustang. When we got back, we had to start packing to go since we were leaving the next day.

We had to get plenty of sleep the night before we left. We woke up early to get ready to leave. We got back on the plane in New York City and headed back to Tennessee. My grandma picked us up from the airport. Then we got in our own car and headed back home. What a fun trip!!

## Rainforest

*Josie Spivey*
*Blackman Elementary School, Grade 4*

Dripping wet
Exotic
Super far away
Tall trees
Indonesia has a large area of rainforest
Not where people live
Awesome animals
Tropic of Capricorn to Tropic of Cancer
Insects galore
Only six percent of the world's land surface
Nature's best

# I Remember

*Taylor Jordan*
*Homer Pittard Campus School, Grade 6*


I remember waiting to get on the plane.
And I remember wanting to get to Colorado really badly.

I remember the two-hour drive to the small town where we were staying.
And I remember all the time it took to get there.

I remember arriving at the condo where we were staying.
And I remember loving how warm and cozy it was.

I remember the two feet of snow outside.
And I remember the frozen swimming pool.

I remember falling down a lot at first.
And I remember getting better and better.

I remember our flight home being delayed four hours.
And I remember watching basketball in airport.


# Destination: Nowhere

*Jessica Patel*
*Christiana Middle School, Grade 7*

I am erasing myself,
Forgetting everyone and everything.
My mind is free and floating.
My soul is free to sing!
My thoughts are wandering.
I'm thinking about nothing.
I'm in the middle of nowhere,
And then my thoughts take wing.
My thoughts are forming a place,
A place I know nothing of.
The grass is green, the flowers alive,
Just me, the ground, and heaven above.
The trees are extremely tall.
The golden leaves are carrying me away.
Then, swish, swish, swish!
I've reached my destination – a brand new day!

## My Final Destination

*Abby Waldron*
*Blackman Middle School, Grade 8*


I believe I have walked all this way,
   Just to be with God in Heaven some day
He has chosen many, and one of them is me.
   I want to live God's way so others will see
How a place like heaven must be a wonderful sight.
   I want to show them how to walk in the light.
What an indescribable place heaven must be,
    That is my final destination.
I hope others will come with me.


## A Magic Carpet Ride

*Jessie Kearney*
*Blackman Elementary School, Grade 2*

    Once upon a time, a girl named Jessie found a magic carpet. She got on and it took her to a far away place. It was covered in lions! Jessie was afraid. She screamed out loud! All the lions roared at her. One lion named Jada said, "Don't be afraid. We want to be your friend! We don't have very many visitors; we get lonely."
    Oh, no! Jessie was turning into a lion. She was fast. A lion named Carston said, "You will become a lion soon! You better go home, go now!"
    Jessie ran to the magic carpet and took off quickly. Soon she was home again. She wrote stories about the lions, especially Jada.


## Beach

*Alyssa Leigh Wright*
*Blackman Elementary School, Grade 5*


**B**lue sky
**E**xciting
**A**rtistic
**C**rashing waves
**H**ot

## Las Vegas

*Hailey Lopez*
*Blackman Elementary School, Grade 4*

Desert climate
Everywhere there are activities
Some fun is found for kids
Temperature is warm
Interesting entertainment
Nighttime is still bright
Air is polluted
Tall buildings
Intriguing
Operating city
Nighttime is noisy
Sight-seeing

## Family Fun

*Zackary Bowden*
*Blackman Elementary School, Grade 2*

My family and I took a cruise with some of our friends and neighbors. The name of our ship was The Fantasy. We all had a lot of fun and a lot of different kinds of food. We visited the country of Mexico, which was cool.

I'm looking forward to another trip when I get a little older. We took a lot of pictures and met plenty of fun people. I really love my mom and dad for taking our family on this vacation.

**The French Ship** • *Brenda Ochoa* • *Blackman Elementary School, Grade 3*

## Journeys

*Ethan Hall*
*Siegel Middle School, Grade 8*

Raining ash and smoke pour down,
Everywhere, there is confusion. In the
Morning, Pompeii is being rained down upon by
The volcano.
After the eruption is over,
Everyone is dead, no one left.
Just piles of ash and rocks.
Over the years, the rock travels
Everywhere,
riding on storms like a piece of trash in the wind.
Mornings, nights, and days
Left, right, up, and, down.
I felt it before I saw it,
cutting my
Knee.
Jutting out of the ground.
I knew this rock had come from
Somewhere special, seeing its dark, black color,
its sharp edges.
I wondered how this rock had gotten all the way in my
Backyard.
All the way back from somewhere between the
Jurassic Period, and the Great Pompeii Eruption,
And now it is in my rock collection.


## Destinations

*Brittany McCrary*
*Blackman Middle School, Grade 8*

Dream big.
Enjoy life.
See good things and forget the bad.
Think good thoughts.
Imagine.
Never give up.
Always keep your head held high.
Tell yourself you matter.
In times of need, help.
Open your heart to others.
Navigate your DESTINATION!
Say you care.

24

# Destinations from the Alphabet

*Greer Kimbell*
*Blackman Middle School, Grade 8*

My destinations are to . . .
Answer someone's cry for a friend
Be myself, no matter what anyone else thinks
Come to the point of understanding life's purposes
Do the right thing, no matter what
Enjoy life to its fullest extent possible
Find a friend who can sing my song back to me when I have forgotten the words
Graduate high school as a valedictorian
Have a completely carefree day with no worries
Imitate Christ's way of living
Jump into the ocean of opportunities to find new hobbies
Keep looking for ways to improve myself
Love everyone as myself
Make decisions that I will be proud of in the long run
Never forget who and whose I am
Only *share good thoughts* about people, keeping the not-so-good thoughts to myself
Peel off the skin of an orange without completely destroying the orange itself
Quit stressing myself out so much
Read the entire Bible
Sleep under the stars one night
Travel to each continent and learn about each individual culture
Understand everything pertaining to chords in music
View each individual as someone who can contribute something great to the world
Withstand peer pressure
X-out any ideas of failure and keep trying with a good attitude
Yield great results on my final exams
Zoom above and beyond everyone's expectations


# My Trip to Disney World

*Casey Keel*
*Smyrna Primary School, Grade 2*

My family went to Disney World this summer. I rode Splash Mountain. The tea cups spun around and around. We went to Minnie's house. I will always remember this trip with my family!

# The Beach

*Michael Shadowens*
*Christiana Elementary School, Grade 5*

The ocean is stunning
The sky is amazingly clear
I can't wait much longer
I sure hope we are near

I can just hear the waves
Leaping for the shore
The sand is as white as snow
Maybe I won't have to wait anymore

Oh! I see the ocean and the beach
The water is so transparent and the sky is blue
The palm trees are blowing in the breeze
Now my dreams have finally come true

**Relaxing on the Beach** • *Micah Faulk* • *Christiana Elementary School, Grade 5*

# I'm Goin'

*Alexandra Wolohon*
*Siegel Middle School, Grade 8*

I'm goin', goin' somewhere, somewhere great.
Somewere peaceful, loud, pretty, and clean
Paris...China...Scotland...or Florida... a place, any place,
I'm goin' wherever my feet, mind, and heart take me.
I'm goin' somewhere where I can be free,
I'm goin' to a place to let go.
I'm goin'.... I'm goin'.....I'm gone.


# Mars and Earth

*Gabby Colarusso*
*Christiana Elementary School, Grade 3*

When I grow up, I want to study Mars. Mars has frozen ice on it and that makes it very interesting. Some day I really want to travel to Mars, but right now all I do is travel from Tennessee to Pennsylvania.

I wondered why they call Mars the red planet. Well, I found my answer. Mars is all red because of the red dirt on it. Mars can never be like Earth. Mars is smaller than Earth and Mars is red. Earth is bigger and is a beautiful blue and green.

We've studied a lot about these two planets, and that is why I want to visit there.


# The Murfreesboro Song

*Gideon Garcia*
*Stewartsboro Elementary School, Grade 3*

I love Murfreesboro.
It is a great old town.
It is a perfect place.
It never gave me a frown.
I always have a happy face!
It is the greatest place around.

Then men were brought here
To learn to fight in Europe.
It was called maneuvers.
They would fight in World War II.
Murfreesboro has a lot of history.
Handed down for me and you.

# The Journey of a Baseball

*Jacob Schultz*
*Siegel Middle School, Grade 8*

I've been hit in the dirt and soared through the air,
Even tossed around without a care
My seams are loose, my leather worn.
I feel like a stranger, a man forlorn.
The count is full, the tempers high,
The pitcher lets out a definitive sigh.
The bases are empty, the score is tied,
The last inning of this exorbitant strife!
One more out would end the game,
Ending the World Series, ending my pain.
The pitcher grips me, agonizingly tight,
Yet holds me close, like a mother so light.
He stares at the batter who steps to the plate,
His hand boiling hot with rivalry's hate.
He starts his motion, he reels and he throws,
The batter is great, but not on his toes,
I hear a 'whoosh' and raucous cries.
I feel a pain of incredible size.
I'm in the catcher's reliable hands,
As fans go wild from all over the stands.
My pain is over, or so I wish,
At the bottom of a pile,
In the pitcher's fist.
The season is over, and so is the game,
I'm given to a man from the Hall of Fame.

Now here I sit, no more do I play,
On a dusty, old shelf day after day
As a striking emblem
of the batter's dismay.

## Destinations

*Brandon Warrick*
*Christiana Elementary School, Grade 5*

If you could choose a destination, where would you go?

Would you start on a journey that takes you to Tokyo,
       or would you take a cruise across the great wide sea,
       and come ashore in beautiful Hawaii?
But I've also heard of this glorious site,
       the shimmering lights of Paris at night.
So pack your bags to go to new places,
       to meet different people and see new faces.
As for now, I'm going to the Great Wall of China,
       to make memories with my aunt from North Carolina!

## Eagleville, My Destination

*Austin Boardman*
*Eagleville School, Grade 3*

I've had many destinations, but my favorite was to move into my new house. It was a fun time. It all started this past summer vacation. My family was looking for more property. I liked a lot of the houses we saw, but the house we bought was in a little town called Eagleville. I liked this house a lot. It had six acres. The town wasn't very busy, but I liked that. Our house was close enough to school that I could almost walk. At school, I met a lot of friends. The work isn't too hard. The school has a high school, a middle school, and an elementary school. This is a good town. I say this is the best town ever! I have a good life here in Eagleville.

# A True Paradise

*Seth Dean*
*Riverdale High School, Grade 11*

Arise from bed half asleep
Alarm clock never ceasing to beep;
A smile comes over like a subtle wave
Excitement and energy I'll have to save

The bag I lift is oh so soft
It's time to go play me some golf;
I grab the ball, my club, my tee
This is the time for me, just me

To swing long and straight is the job I must do
I look down the fairway at the accretion of dew;
I sway and I waggle to ready my swing
I make contact and hear the harmonious ting

The journey begins to beat my past score
It's times like this that I wish I played more;
Back to the pro-shop half done with my round
It's still early on, I can't hear a sound

Grab a snack and go, there's no time to spare
A tricky choice comes and voices its dare;
I start to feel risky and give it a shot
It skips in the water and cries "Plit plot"

Straight ahead, the parking lot is in sight
The bag on my back is starting to feel tight;
One last putt and the ball hits my club's tip
It turns and curves and rolls in the cup's lip

I jump and rejoice for the new record is mine
The ride home from the course will be that much more fine

# To Know

*Derek Williams*
*Siegel High School, Grade 11*

Here I stand
not knowing where to go
but knowing where I am
not knowing who I'll be
but knowing who I've been

I have stood in the North
I have stood in the South
I have stood in the East and in the West
I have known the warmth of the sun
the cold of the snow
the mighty peaks of white mountains
the gleam of the White City in the morning sun
the cold, golden glint of the immortal emperor's throne
the storms on Hoth, and the dry sand of Tatooine

I have felt the dry, yellow grass of El Paso
the lush, vibrant green grass of Lexington
and the sticky, weedy grass of Murfreesboro

I have felt a ball hit my hands more times than I can count
and I have kicked a ball more times than the world has spun,

I know I stand upon the borders of greatness
or of mediocrity
I know I stand at an impasse
but I do not know were to go from here,
people line both paths
some cheer me on, encouraging with words
others challenge with their silent stares
though none lay behind me
none to push me upon a course

They ask me where I am going
and as an answer, I say I do not know

To shun the constraints set upon
to free myself from tired bonds
to let free all that is within me
and escape from social norms
to live the way I want to
to write what I want to write
to stand where I want to stand and to say all I have to say

but I cannot for fear of wrath
for the fear of failure
for the fear of loneliness

For they want me to tell the future
and folly it is, as we all know.


## The Park
*Courtney Gadbois*
*Christiana Elementary School, Grade 5*

I feel the soft sand
I touch the metal swing
I hear the kids screaming
I see the multi-colored birds
I taste the sweetness of spending time with my family

## Fall Fun
*Abby Garrett*
*Wilson Elementary School, Grade 1*

I went to my grandparents' house. They have a lot of leaves. I swung on a rope and landed in a leaf pile. We burned the leaves and it made lots of smoke. I had fun!


## City of White Buildings
*Lytton Haley*
*Eagleville School, Grade 3*

One of my favorite trips was to Washington, D.C. I went with my parents and brother. I remember going up the escalator into the mall. I was so excited! I thought all the white buildings were beautiful. At night they looked like bright stars in the sky. My favorite building was the Lincoln Memorial.

I think everyone should go to Washington, D.C.

## My Special Vacation

*Danielle Lunsford*
*Blackman Elementary School, Grade 5*

My special vacation would have to be when I went on a cruise. It was awesome! I got to sleep in a bunk. The cruise went to the Bahamas. It was very pretty! The water was very blue and clear. You could even see fish swimming around. My favorite part was eating all the ice cream I wanted for free! It was very special because it was my first cruise and my parents surprised me. That was my most favorite vacation ever!

## Destinations

*Makena Nail*
*Christiana Elementary School, Grade 5*

A destination is…
    a place you are going

A destination can be…
    far over seas or just down the street

A destination can be…
    very interesting or really boring

A destination can be…
    a long journey or quick adventure

A destination can be…
    around the corner or to the moon

A destination is waiting wherever you go!

## Going to the Beach

*Paiton Kaufman*
*David Youree Elementary School, Grade 3*

Sea,
sand,
shells,
fish,
jellyfish,
sharks,
people,
starfish,
turtles,
bluefish.

# Solo

*Gracie Bryson*
*Siegel High School, Grade 12*

Leading with pointed toes and a praying heart,
I glide onto the stage.
Many have made their mark on this platform,
But they are forgotten now as all eyes follow my movement.
My head is lifted high over my shoulders.
Confidence shines through my countenance,
Masking the deafening beats of my heart.

The familiar music permeates my being.
I hear my Coach's voice,
"I am so proud of how far you've come."
Taking a deep breath,
I begin to dance.

Tears and smiles and fears and hopes defined my journey
To the stage life led me.
Blisters were replaced by calluses.
Limitations were cast out by growth.
Incompetence was trampled over by drive.
Sustained by the love and support of my parents,
I improved.
Finally, I am able to take these steps.

As the song draws closer to its end,
My eyes flood.
How can I hold on to this moment?
It has come,
My time on this stage is complete.
I block out the applause to hear,
"Well done, my child."

Leading with pointed toes,
I slowly make my way off this stage toward the open door.
And my heart is still dancing.
Dancing.

## My Vacation

*Corneilus Johnson*
*Blackman Elementary School, Grade 5*

One time I went to Disney World. It was a very special trip because it was my birthday. My favorite memory was when I drove a go-kart and got into a huge traffic jam. I also enjoyed going on the backlot tour. It was a tour of all the movie props. That was the most special vacation I ever had.

## The Next Step

*Abigail Thenthirath*
*LaVergne Lake Elementary School, Grade 4*

I have moved three times. From Massachusetts to Connecticut, then all the way to Tennessee. I had to pass five states. They are New York, New Jersey, Pennsylvania, West Virginia, and Virginia. Each state has great places. All the souvenirs were perfect. It was a non-stop trip. All I could think of was getting to my destination!

Staying in a car for two days is painful, but all this hard work will be paid off at the end. I just didn't know that. Now that I am here, the schools are great and I am glad I moved here.

## Destinations

*Selena Alejandro*
*Blackman Elementary School, Grade 3*

It means a place you are going. It could be a vacation, a career, or just a place in your town. Getting to your destination can be exciting, because it's a journey that can bring adventure. Or a destination can just be a point in your life you want to accomplish.

# Seasons of Change
*Baylee Busbee*
*Blackman Elementary School, Grade 3*

Florida used to be my home.
Then we decided to pack up and roam.
We drove and drove, and drove all night.
When I woke up, I saw a gorgeous sight.
We had arrived in Tennessee.
With so many new things to see.
In Florida everything was so green.
But here that isn't the only color seen.
Orange, green, yellow, and red.
Those colors are falling on my head.
Soon there will be snow and then flowers.
And I will play outside for hours.
I'm so glad that I moved to Tennessee.
Now my family and I are as happy as can be.


# The Path Traveled
*Amber Williams*
*Siegel High School, Grade 12*

      The postmark declares the letter to have traveled at least from Colorado to Tennessee. Linda, a friend for several years, is skiing in Aspen before returning home from another world tour. The letter describes her journey through the southern parts of Asia and some island-hopping in the Pacific Ocean. She goes on and on, eventually telling me she wishes I had been there, how much I would have enjoyed the trip.

      I lay the letter on the counter as the oven timer starts screeching. Oven mitt goes on one hand. The oven is turned off, *click,* with the other as I simultaneously open the stove. Heat blasts out, warming my face. I remove the pan, *clang, clang,* and place it on top of the cold burners to cool. The pot of noodles boiling nearby threatens to overflow. I turn that particular stove eye down. Having retrieved a spoon, I stir until the foam crusted top settles down. I toss in some spices, just to keep things exciting.

      A strand of my hair is pushed back behind my ear. I tuck the letter into its envelope, tossing it onto a nearby counter. Linda's voice still follows me as I set the dinner table. "Oh, dearest Amanda, you have no idea what it is like to see such destinations. Remember all those nights in our dorm room when we talked about traversing the globe? When we tried to imagine how amazing it would be to do all those exotic things we read about in those journals? Well, the experiences are far better than anything on this glorious planet. Nothing can compare!"

      I survey my work, my thoughts now only of the work at hand. Each napkin folded with careful attention to every fold. The cups are filled to the perfect height, the right amount of ice to please the individual's personal taste. Plates centered in the middle of placemats, everything set on the table in line with all the other objects due to some OCD tendencies among the diners. "Ok," I say to no one in particular.

"Everything's ready." I leave the dining room to announce the decision to everyone.

The scene I walk into in the next room causes me to stop, silent. A man, so wonderful in many ways, holds a precious baby boy in one arm while playing one of those mini-xylophones with a three year old. The man hits a small series of notes. *Dee, da, dee, dum.* The youngest giggles while the three year old copies the notes, hitting two notes at once, shrieking with laughter. "Close enough, buddy," the father says, ruffling the boy's golden blonde hair.

"Michael, how about you bring those boys over here for some dinner?"

He sniffs the air dramatically. "I don't know." He gets up, motioning for the toddler to follow. "Smells like I shouldn't."

"Hahaha." He kisses me on the forehead as I take the baby from his arms.

I play with the small little feet of my son before looking toward the table. Michael tucks a napkin into the shirt of his firstborn, talking gently to him. Ok, maybe I have not been able to follow Linda across the globe. Moments like this, moments with my children, moments with my husband, moments doing all the behind-the-scenes work, they all trump her experiences. Michael looks up at me and winks. I blow him a kiss as I situate the infant in his high chair. "This food is delicious, Amanda. Better than anything one can find in Italy."

I smile. *Welcome to the greatest destination on Earth.*

**The White Forest** • *Aldair Avalos-Madera* • *Blackman Elementary School, Grade 5*

Chapter Two

# Memories of Friends and Family

## My Dad

*Austin Hughes*
*Blackman Middle School, Grade 6*

I miss my dad
Now that he is gone.
He never said I was bad
And my memories of him are fond.
I love him very much.
I miss his hugs and touch.
He was my light and joy.
He played with me like a boy.
I love you Dad with all my heart.
I remember when we played with darts.
Now you are in Texas and you have a new wife.
It seems like you are starting a whole new life.

## Pappy

*Ben Kimball*
*Lascassas Elementary School, Grade 5*

I like my pappy.
He makes me happy
When he goes hunting.
He wears a cappie.
When he gets tired
He takes a nappy!

**Papa** • *Maddy Bridges* • *Cedar Grove Elementary School, Grade 3*

## My Dad

*Henry Orr*
*Walter Hill Elementary School, Grade 3*

I remember my dad and what happened to him. When my dad went to work, I would sit at home. Then he came home, and we would play with each other all night long. But once, he never came home. He had gotten into a car wreck and died. It happened five years ago. We both really loved each other and will never stop.

## My Sister

*Sarah Bleam*
*Stewarts Creek Middle School, Grade 7*

My sister is not a superhero,
someone who's always on TV.

She might be a normal person to you,
but she's so much more to me.

She's a person you'd see in every grocery store,
but underneath what you see is a heart worth so much more.

She's kind, caring, and understanding,
she knows when something's not right.

I know she knows what she's talking about,
even when we fight.

She seems wiser than the owls that sit up in the tree,
she's the best sister anyone could have or ever be.

If she sees me doing something wrong, she'll tell me right away.
We may sometimes argue, but she listens to what I say.

It seems like I could never measure up to the great things she's done.
She's done so many things and she's only just begun.

People know her for being "Smiley" and a leader for all.
She's also very beautiful, with blue eyes and tall.

I can't believe I have her for a sister and a friend!
Hannah, I love you, and that will never end.

# My Mother

*Jeneylise Santiago*
*Cedar Grove Elementary School, Grade 4*

I am thankful because I have really had a lot of adventures in my life and I am glad because I have learned a lot of lessons. I have learned right and wrong. I appreciate my mom for having me.

My mom is different from any other mom. I believe that a mother is the heart of a home. She treats each child equally, but somehow makes each one feel special in her own way. My mom has given me and my sisters a special gift. My mom has given me the gift of being a blessing to me. My mom makes me stronger every day and confident. That's why I love her and appreciate her. I hope she keeps on blessing me and teaching me new things. I love her very much!

# My Mom

*Chance Curran*
*Walter Hill Elementary School, Grade 2*

I love my mommy.
She cooks me food,
And she always knows what to do.
My mommy is a very special girl.
She is the best in the world.

# Friend

*Morgan Wilcoxson*
*Lascassas Elementary School, Grade 5*

You make me smile.
You make me laugh.
You cheer me up when I'm sad.
You always help me when I'm stuck.
You are my hero now and forever.
You buy me things.
You love me a lot.
I am writing this poem because you mean a lot.

# Mommy and Me

*Amariah Kenney*
*Walter Hill Elementary School, Grade 2*

Mommy loves me.
I love Mommy.
She feeds me every day.
She kisses me every night.
Mommy and me
Together forever.
Mommy and me.


# A Visit to Grandma's House

*Haylie Padgett*
*Lascassas Elementary School, Grade 3*


As I walked to Grandma's house
I was filled with joy
As I looked there she was standing outside the door
I hugged her
When I did, my eyes began to water
I came in and ate some of her homemade cookies
Then soon it was time to go
Before I left, I gave her a big hug
I looked back
Both of our eyes began to water


# My Friend Bailey

*Chloe Heath*
*Blackman Elementary School, Grade 3*

Being truthful about everything
Always sticks by my side
I love to play with her
Loves the same things as me
Everybody loves her
You couldn't ask for a better friend

# My Mom

*Kerri Phillips*
*Blackman Elementary School, Grade 2*


My mom is the best person in the world. Is your mom the best? She helps me with everything! She helps me put on my clothes, clean myself, and she helps me brush my hair. That's why I love my mom!


# China

*Lena Farris*
*Blackman Middle School, Grade 6*


Clara came from
Here.
In a month we were back
Never forget
Always will love her.


# Two Peas in a Pod

*Gabi Gumucio*
*Stewarts Creek Middle School, Grade 7*

Even if the world came to an end,
My mom will always be my best friend,

I can talk to her about anything in my head,
We usually talk when I get tucked into bed,

We like to listen to music on long trips in the car,
So that concludes my statement that two peas in a pod is truly what we are.

# My Family Tree

*Liam Page*
*McFadden School of Excellence, Grade 6*

First we will start with my mother
She is unlike any other
She cares, loves and gives to me
She is the kindest in my family tree

Now we will go to my dad
Not once has he made me sad
He's kind and strong and protective of me
He is the most fun in my family tree

Here we go with my sister
I love her although she's quite a screamer
She is the best to keep one company
No doubt she's the warmest in my family tree

And now we have my little brother
He is DEFINITELY unlike any other
He's smart and annoying, evil and happy
He is the greatest friend in my family tree

Everyone loves these wonderful people
They are kind and loving and just a little bit evil
If anyone doesn't like my family tree
Just watch them say that to <u>ME</u>

And there you have my family tree
Greatest people in the world to me
And if you ever get to meet 'em
Tell them what I think about them


# My Friend Nealey

*M'Avia Bell*
*Cedar Grove Elementary School, Grade 3*

Nealey is my friend
She is so helpful to me
She makes my heart smile.

## My Grandpa

*Joshua Lattin*
*Smyrna Primary School, Grade 1*

My grandpa is a veteran. He was stationed in Germany.
His brother was also a veteran. My dad was named after him.
Having veterans in my family makes me fee proud. Our
Veterans make us all feel **proud** to be **Americans.**


## The Truth

*Blake Slaughter*
*Cedar Grove Elementary School, Grade 4*

Some people might not believe what I am about to write because of the way I am always making jokes about my brother, BUT, I love him. Even though I say I hate him that is out of anger, not from the heart. He may get on my nerves but that's just what little brothers do. Also, when I say I wish he wasn't born, that is out of anger.

My little brother and I have had our good times and our bad, but in the end we always get along. Like on Sunday, he would not stop asking me if he could play Smack Down vs. Raw 2008. I told him today was the first day that the invention of Smack Down vs. Raw 2009 ever came out and if I got it, I would let him play the 2008 version. Yesterday he started begging me again and I said, "Just take it." I made a promise that he could play it whenever he wanted and I am going to keep that promise. So far, I have kept it.


## My Best Friend

*Joelle Patton*
*Blackman Elementary School, Grade 1*

Allie is my best friend.

She helps me sometimes when I get hurt.

We go to football games together.

## Haley's Hope
*Haley Byrd*
*Cedar Grove Elementary School, Grade 1*

McKayla is my best friend. We have been friends since we were born. She got cancer two times. I was sad when she was sick because we could not play. I went to visit her at the hospital. I would color with her. She lost all her hair but she was still pretty to me, and I love her so much. She is better now and my hope is that she stays better.

Best Friends Forever, Haley and McKayla


## Grandpa's Watch
*Daniel Uss*
*Rockvale Middle School, Grade 6*

Everybody enjoys getting a gift. All gifts have something in common. And that is that all gifts are special. I once got a gift so special it meant the world to me. It was my grandpa's watch. The reason why it was so special was because his grandpa wore it when he was a kid. My grandpa gave it to me when I was seven. I remember the words that came out of his mouth, "I want you to have this watch. It means so much to me, now I want you to have it."

I've had that watch ever since. I have it in my room in a glass box on my night stand. I remember all the fun we used to have. When I look at it I remember him as more than just my grandpa. I remember him as a best friend; someone who was always there for me, someone who would never say no. He truly was a friend. And I will always remember him.


## Grandma
*Harleigh McNeely*
*Blackman Elementary School, Grade 3*

Great at baking
Responsible person
An excellent sense of humor
Never lets me down
Down right perfect
Most wonderful grandma ever
A great woman

48

## Finally Home

*Jessica Wilson*
*Oakland High School, Grade 12*

Walking down the lonely road,
carrying a heavy load
of worry, trouble, and despair
handling it with the utmost care.
Through twisted paths and gnarled tree roots
listening to the horned owl's hoots.
Trying hard not to slip and fall
wondering if I will get there at all.
Unable to stop and take a break
on I go, though I start to shake.
Getting closer, I know I must,
but my body's failing and hard to trust.
Walking faster, running now
it seems so far, but I don't know how.
Suddenly a house comes into my view
its image upon me is stuck like glue.
Slowly but surely, the door opens with a groan.
I close my eyes with a smile, I am finally home.

**Focus on the Destination** • *Kirstie Pike* • *Siegel High School, Grade 11*

## Mom

*Nicholas Gardner*
*Blackman Elementary School, Grade 3*

My mom cares for me with all her heart.
Outrageously great, and always over the top.
My mom likes me for who I am.


## A Paved Path

*Miguel Rodriguez*
*Smyrna High School, Grade 11*

Every path is measured by achievements and failures,
Every path is accompanied by situations and pleasures,
Unfortunately, my path began with tragedy's caring hands,
A burden bestowed that illuminates our captivity,
The price we pay that shapes our future activity

What defines us all?
Our characteristics

The life that cannot be lived by minor statistics,
As my brother's paralysis has taught me,
Life is filled more of choices than of prophecies,
As I have grown,
I have realized that a future is paved from experiences that we have endured,
And ultimately that path leads us to hopes and dreams we wish to be ensured.

As I regret that the experience, too, comes from heartache and pain,
It elaborates on the success that will keep us sane.
This tragic event is listed on every application I submit to a university,
As I know it is my true individuality and diversity

However, as I walk my path,
I cannot help but wonder

Am I my brother's keeper?
This is the question that traces the border stones of my future path…

## My Family

*Addison Love*
*Cedar Grove Elementary School, Grade 1*

My family is the greatest of all families. My family always has time for me. We do tons of fun stuff like playing sports in the backyard together. Sometimes we sleep out in the living room just like we were going camping. The reason that I think they are so great is because they love me a whole lot.

## My Family

*Cynthia Guzman*
*Cedar Grove Elementary School, Grade 1*

My family is special to me because they help me when I can't do something on my own, especially my mom. I also have two brothers and my dad. Someday, I will be an artist.

## Grandparents

*Kendyl Ford*
*Cedar Grove Elementary School, Grade 3*

Grandparents are great
They make you very happy
Yes, they are so sweet.

## My Grandad

*Gabriel Thompson*
*Smyrna Primary School, Grade 1*

I want to be just like my grandad when I grow up. He has a good job and makes a lot of money. He is a janitor at a school in another city. We go to church together. After church, we have fun eating and talking at a special restaurant. I love my grandad!

## I Am Thankful

*Alejandra Ledezma*
*Smyrna Primary School, Grade 1*

I am very thankful for my mom and dad. They work to make my life easy and fun. Mom and Dad keep me safe from danger. I am thankful for my teacher, too! She makes learning fun, and that is why I make super grades and honor roll!

## My House

*Abigail Ridinger*
*Blackman Elementary School, Grade 4*

I remember my house!
I smell great cooking, air freshner!
I hear the TV talking, laughter, loud barking!
I see kids fighting roughly, dad cooking, dogs, video games!
I touch the TV, lamps, carpets, blankets, humongous floors!
I feel wonderful, much loved, secure!
I remember my house!

# A Family in August

*Derek Craker*
*Smyrna High School, Grade 11*

It happened one week,
Every twelve months,
For ten years
When I really felt like I belonged.
Taking in the air of a Michigan morning
At a family reunion in August

August: my chance to be with my family.
A family separated by a hundred miles
Who are only a memory of the August before.

My chance before a week would pass,
Where a car ride home would override my
Wish of endless time.

Twelve months where a damp and cloudy
Chicago sky would taunt my longing of a summer
Sun rising from its slumber on Traverse Bay.

Now, although separated five hundred miles,
Brought to Tennessee,
And left for Time to decide,
It is my family of August
That I will always belong.


# The Day My Brother Was Born

*Kateland Ward*
*Walter Hill Elementary School, Grade 3*

I was three years old when it happened. I was at home with my Nana. My mom and dad were at the hospital. The next thing I know my Nana got a phone call from the hospital. She gets off the phone and says, "Katie, you have a baby brother."

We went to the hospital. I got to see my baby brother. Then we brought him home. It was the next day when I got to hold him. My mom let me feed him sometimes. When she fed him, I got to burp him. Sometimes my mom would let me come with her to change his diaper. Then we moved to Middle Tennessee. It was almost the same until the day he quit breathing. He was rushed to the hospital. They saved him, and his name is Riley. That's how I have a brother today.

## Missing My Uncle

*Caitlyn Miller*
*Christiana Elementary School, Grade 5*

**G**reat view of the lake
**A**wesome time with my Uncle C.W.
**T**ime to go to bed
**L**ove him a lot
**I** miss him so much
**N**ever going to forget him
**B**oth of us used to play all day
**U**ncle, I miss you
**R**ough times for all of us
**G**reat times with you


## An Inspiration

*Savannah Towe*
*Christiana Elementary School, Grade 5*

My brother Joshua Andrew Towe is an inspiration to me. He is eighteen turning nineteen next year. He has a wife Amanda, and they just had a daughter November second. He is in the Navy, and a few months ago he graduated from school. He taught me to be a good sport. He taught me all of the techniques of drawing. My brother is a real inspiration to me.


## I Love My Family

*Gabriella Hunt*
*Blackman Elementary School, Grade 2*

My family is special to me because they love and care for me. At any time, they always love me no matter what. They always spend time with me. Sometimes we go shopping. Every time I go to bed, they hug and kiss me goodnight. I'll always love them.

# I Remember Grandmamma and Granddaddy's House
*Emma Demonbreun*
*Homer Pittard Campus School, Grade 6*


I remember making plays and performing them with my cousins in the basement.
And I remember arguing over who got the lead role.

I remember opening the traditional Christmas box.
And I remember drawing numbers to see who would go first.

I remember baking cakes with Grandmamma when I was little.
And I remember climbing on the counter to help mix the batter.

I remember staying up late with my cousins talking about tomorrow.
And I remember Grandmamma telling us to be quiet.

I remember painting the fence with Granddaddy.
And I remember wearing baggy clothes borrowed from the drawer so I wouldn't get my clothes messy.

I remember birthday bonfires with cousins in the field.
And I remember roasting marshmallows and making s'mores.

I remember good times at Grandmamma and Granddaddy's house.
And I remember the love I receive there.


# The Sleepy Heads
*Gracie Bell*
*Homer Pittard Campus School, Grade 4*


My family lives inside a bed.
My dad is the mattress
Nice, comfy, and strong.
My mom is the pillow
Soft, sweet, and never wrong.
My siblings are the sheets
Warm, loving, and kind.
And I am the person who sleeps
Safe all the time.

## My Family
*Kate Roden*
*Stewarts Creek Middle School, Grade 6*

For all of my life I've had two very loving parents. They've been with me through good times and bad times. When I come home I know they will be waiting for me with open arms. If I've had a bad day, they will sit down and listen to me. If I've had a good day, they will be happy too. My greatest memories are with them. We all know how to make each other smile. I love my family!


## My Mother
*Makayla Jones*
*Blackman Elementary School, Grade 3*

Making sure I'm okay when I fall down on the ground
Often hugging me and loving me forever and always
Thinking of ways to help me learn in a fun way
Helping me with my homework when I need help
Every time that I have trouble she helps me.
Reading words with me if I need help


## I Love My Family, Yes I Do
*Chloe Bowen*
*David Youree Elementary School, Grade 3*

I love my family, yes I do. I also love my friends too.
How about you? Do you love someone? If you don't, you need some work to be done.
If you don't get work done, you won't have a girl or a son. I love my family, yes I do. I also love my friends too.

## Parents

*Delaney King*
*Blackman Elementary School, Grade 3*

**P**opular
**A**wesome
**R**eligious
**E**xciting
**N**ormal
**T**rustworthy
**S**ensible


## Fun at Nashville Shores

*Brandon Good*
*Blackman Elementary School, Grade 2*

My mom, dad, Taylor, Uncle David, and I went to Nashville Shores in July. This was a special time because now I have a fun memory of Uncle David.

There was a giant slide called the Hippo and my dad went down with me. Next, I went on the Big Scream! It looked fun, but it was so scary we lost our screaming voices.

I'll remember it because we have pictures. I am thankful we have them since my Uncle David died this September. He was a lot of fun and silly!

**My Memory** • *Prater Christiansen* • *Lascassas Elementary School, Grade 1*

57

## The Picture

*Emily Thompson*
*Siegel High School, Grade 12*

I stare at a picture of my best friends and me
Wondering, in a year, just how close we will be
When in different directions we each have gone
New experiences and challenges we must face all alone

These past four years we've grown so much
In each other's arms, found a comforting touch
When life has given us lessons to learn
It's to each other we've always turned

I love them dearly, this is true
Friends like these are far and few
At first glance, we're different as can be
But really perfect complements, anyone can see

I wonder, without them by my side
How through life I'll be able to glide
Without their constant comforting presence
Will I ever find such priceless resonance?

I wonder these things, but deep down I know
My shallow fears should not toss me to and fro
Much deeper is my love for these friends
Than any change could ever hope to bend

As with everything we've been dealt
Our time apart will not cause us to melt
On different paths to different destinations
This curve is just another exploration

## A Special Time

*Kalyn Choate*
*Blackman Elementary School, Grade 2*

Last weekend, I went to my great aunt's 90th birthday party in South Carolina. Some of my family came from Arizona to be there. I got to meet my cousins for the first time. We had the whole restaurant to ourselves. I got to toast my great aunt with sparkling grape juice. It was lots of fun.

## Megan and I

*Chloe Blanton*
*Wilson Elementary School, Grade 2*

One day when I grow up, my friend Megan and I will go to Texas. We will go to a cool hotel and stay up all night. We will eat good food, like cake, because we love cake. Then we will play all night, and we will have fun. My brothers will have to stay at home while Megan and I have tons of fun! We will go to shops and buy stuff, like some shoes and shirts and then go back to the hotel. While we are at the hotel, we will go to bed at 1:00 in the morning. At 7:00 we will go to eat breakfast.

## My Book

*Miranda Reed*
*Homer Pittard Campus School, Grade 4*

My mom is the cover,
To hold us together.
My Dad the title,
To give us a name.
My sister the author,
Who writes my book.
My brother the illustrator,
Who brings our story to life.
My dog the spine,
Who protects our family.
Me the pages,
Who tells our story.

## A Special Friend

*Maiah Case*
*Barfield Elementary School, Grade 3*

This year I met a new friend named Gwen James. Gwen is very nice. I sometimes help her with her work. She sits next to me in my class. When we go outside, I push her on the walking track. Her wheel chair is red and her little wheels light up in the front. I hope Gwen and I are friends forever!

# Thanksgiving Dinner

*Alyssa Hamilton*
*LaVergne Middle School, Grade 6*

Right as I was going to sit at my grandmother's table, I felt a mix of mashed potatoes, macaroni, and ketchup being squished in my hair. This goes along with one of my fondest memories. My fondest memory is Thanksgiving dinner 2006 because my family had a food fight, my uncle brought a turkey, and I got to see family I seldom do.

Thanksgiving dinner is my fondest memory because my family and I had a food fight. My sister had started it by squishing mashed potatoes, macaroni, and ketchup in my hair. Then all the family got in on it and green beans and lettuce were flying through the air. Then my parents got mad, really mad. But overall I got the best throw in on the fight!

Another reason Thanksgiving dinner is a fond memory of mine is because my uncle had brought a turkey. The turkey was a joke though. The turkey my uncle brought was brown and big with red, orange, and yellow feathers. My family could not stop laughing. But the worst thing of all was the turkey kept us up all night long squeaking and squawking.

One more reason that Thanksgiving dinner is one of my fondest memories is I get to spend time with family I never get to see. For instance, I never get to see my Aunt Janice in Florida. My Uncle Steve in the Virgin Islands and a bunch of other people in different states and countries come to spend Thanksgiving with us. Plus Thanksgiving is the only time they come to Tennessee, so it's a special time. Another plus to having family down is everyone brings presents. I hope some time I can go for Thanksgiving dinner where they live.

Thanksgiving will always be my favorite memory because my family and I had a food fight, and that is rare! Another reason Thanksgiving would be my fondest memory is my uncle brought a huge turkey. One more reason Thanksgiving will always be my fondest memory is I get to spend time with all my family. I hope all Thanksgivings-to-come are as special as this one.


# My Special Uncles

*Savannah McCann*
*Walter Hill Elementary School, Grade 2*

I have two very special uncles. They are my great uncles. They were in the Army. They were in the Vietnam War, and they survived. Their names are Ronnie and Goob (his real name is Jerry), but I call him Goob. They are special to me because they love me and we have fun together. This summer Uncle Ronnie died. He was sick with lung cancer. His funeral was very, very sad. All of my family was crying. He had a flag on his casket, and people folded it and gave it to Uncle Goob. Uncle Goob lives by himself now, and sometimes he misses Uncle Ronnie. I wish Uncle Goob lived closer to us so I could see him more. I miss him, and I love him.

# Waffles

*Will Moss*
*Homer Pittard Campus School, Grade 4*

My dad had just gotten brain cancer. He woke me up early in the morning. We were walking outside when my mom asked us where we were going. My dad said, "Myrtle Beach."

My mom said, "I'll get Catie and Matt".

My dad said, "I just want to go with Will."

My mom said, "You can't go. What if something bad happens?" Finally, my mom said, "Ok."

So my dad and I got into the car. We drove past Waffle House. I asked him why we passed it. He said because he was taking me to the one in Myrtle Beach, SC. So we drove and drove down the Main Street of Myrtle Beach, SC. We stopped and ate at Captain Joe's. Then we got a sand bucket at the Sea Shack and built a sand castle and collected seashells. Then my dad bought some ice cream. It was time to go home, so we got in the car and drove back home. When we got home, my mom was mad but happy that we got back home ok. It was a fun trip and one that I will always remember. My dad is now dead. He died on June 23, 2005.


# My Hero, My Mom

*Madelynn McCall*
*Lascassas Elementary School, Grade 4*

Dear Mom,

You are the best mom in the world. You take good care of me. You feed me good food, and you love me a lot. I will always think of you as my hero! Even though you are a parent, I say you are a superhero! My mom, my hero!

Love,
Madelynn

## My Baby Sister

*Devin McKnight*
*Lascassas Elementary School, Grade 4*


It was July 2, 2003, and I was in the hospital waiting room with my grandparents and my brother. We were hoping that my new little sister would soon be born! It was so hard to wait, just sitting and sitting and sitting. We were so tired and hungry, but we were told that we couldn't leave in case my sister came while we were gone. Luckily, we found a snack machine!

We walked to see my mom, but still no baby. We stopped to look at the other babies, played in the hallway, and finally went back to the waiting room. Suddenly, my dad came in and told us that the girl had come! Her name was Lauren.

We waited to see my mom and her, and then my grandparents took my brother and me home with them. My mom had to stay at the hospital for the night. I couldn't wait for her to come home with my new little sister.


## Russell and Me

*Garrett Kaumeyer*
*Blackman Elementary School, Grade 2*

When I lived in Texas, I had a friend named Russell. We went to the same school. We did sports together. We played together all the time. But one day my mom and dad told me we were moving to Tennessee. I was sad. Now I write Russell a note sometimes.


## Grandpa

*Blake Howland*
*Lascassas Elementary School, Grade 5*

Dear Grandpa,

I always have fun with you. I remember coming to your house as a child. We always spent special time together, going on long walks, listening to stories, and making special snacks. We had fun no matter what we did. I can remember singing silly songs, finding and playing with bugs and frogs, collecting rocks and leaves, planting tomatoes, watching the deer, and playing basketball. My favorite memories are of the rainy days when we would cuddle close together and read books. Thanks for making me feel special.

Love,
Blake

# My Treasure

*Codi Tracy*
*Eagleville School, Grade 8*

Everyone has a treasure of their own. It maybe a key chain, a ball, or something like that. My treasure is my family because they are always there for me when I need them the most. They know how I feel almost all the time. They are the ones who understand me the most because they have to put up with me almost all the time. I have a whole lot of people in my family, 38 to be exact, so if I need to go to talk to one of them and they are busy, I just move right on along to the next person. Even though we may have our ups and downs, which rarely happens, they will always be there for me no matter what. When I come home mad from school or somewhere, I know that I can come home to a loving family.

You see, last year something happened that changed my life for good. My parents got a divorce. I don't really like to talk about it much, but sometimes people start to talk about it and you can't help but talk, too. While it was going on, my family was there for everyone who was going through the pain, especially us kids. Even though we still feel pain sometimes, we know that we can talk to one another. The people I consider that were there for me the most are my two older sisters, my cousin Kayla, and my nanny and papa. They were the ones who made sure I was feeling good at all times. Now that it has been almost a year, my two older sisters, my little brother, and I live with my dad. Even though my dad doesn't like to talk to my mom because of what she did, they try to talk and be nice to each other for us kids. We see our mom sometimes on the weekends. Even though she is gone I still consider her part of my treasure no matter what anyone says. I love everyone in my family and if there is ever a problem, I want to try to fix it because I can't stand when we are mad at each other. This is why my family is my treasure, because they would give their own life for mine.

# My New Baby Brother

*Haven Baer*
*Wilson Elementary School, Grade 1*

Hi. My name is Haven. Soon I'm going to have a baby brother! I will be a great big sister. His name is going to be Aidan! I can feed him! I know he is going to be a great brother!

# Friends

*Julissa Martin*
*Stewarts Creek Middle School, Grade 6*

Friends are like sisters
They do everything together
If one cries, the other sheds tears;
If one moves away, the other goes chasing after her.
Friends live on till the very end!

63

# Am I Ready?

*Sara Dusenberry*
*Siegel High School, Grade 12*

I am from no memories of Fort Bragg, North Carolina
And the memory of a long kitchen in Albuquerque, New Mexico
And many memories of a cramped kitchen, of a rock that seemed like a mountain, and
Of a room that looked like me in Murfreesboro, Tennessee.

I am from the love of my parents, John and Madeline Dusenberry,
And the kindness of an older sister, Jennifer Dusenberry and
The sarcasm experienced since birth.

I am from the early morning rides to school in a freezing van and
A fifty dollar savings bond nowhere to be found and
The amazement of my curly hair, so intriguing to others.

I am from the dirt of a softball field and
The smiley faces so encompassing of my attention and
The long weekends spent at the fields playing until the team can give no more and
The excitement of that championship game you have worked so hard to reach.

I am from the tucking of shirts and the looping of belts and
The lack of flip flops that are still seldom worn today and
The lack of a wave so dear to my sister and
The long walks to a high school I couldn't wait to attend.

I come from the conditioning in temperatures below freezing and
The many mornings spent trying to drown out the pro-tooled pop of my fellow
teammates
And the many hours spent working on homework that never seems to end and
The studying for my first AP tests so eager to make it into Mr. Bowman's five club.

I come from the concerts I've experienced and
One long weekend of music heaven and
The finding of people who enjoy the music I find so dear to my heart and
The explanations of how my music is not weird to those who just can't seem to
comprehend.

This is what I come from, but what I want to know is where will I go next?

## My Dad's Truck

*Dallas Hanson*
*Blackman Elementary School, Grade 5*

"Take me away to your secret place; take me away, take me away," I sang with my dad's radio. It was in April around lunch except this was seven years ago. I was riding in my dad's truck on his job. He let me talk to other drivers. My dad and I were on the road 24/7 but at least we were together and nobody can change that.

## My Daddy

*Hatham Al-Hajiri*
*Cedar Grove Elementary School, Grade 3*

Do you like me as I like you?
And I really love you.
Dad you are doing your best.
Do your job as best as you can.
You are a yawning monster but you are the best.

**Speedy** • *Summer Souvannaseng* • *Blackman Elementary School, Grade 2*

65

## My Best Friend Emily Stacey
*Cayce Nutt*
*Blackman Elementary School, Grade 2*

Emily is my favorite person because she is my best friend. We play on the playground together and have lots of play dates. I also have sleepovers with her. We always listen to each other and if one of us gets hurt we help each other. She is sweet and thoughtful. That's why Emily Stacey is my best friend.

## Dad
*Bryce Gard*
*Blackman Elementary School, Grade 3*

My dad's name is Bill; he is a staff sergeant. He is a crew chief for the Blackhawk helicopters. He has been to Iraq, and he will be going back in March 2009. He works on computers for the Army, too. I am very proud of my dad.

## Brothers and Sisters
*Eli Cramer*
*Homer Pittard Campus School, Grade 1*

We're going to start with....
my sister. Well, my sister screams... A LOT!!
And I always have to say, "Will you stop!!"
and my brother eh, ... he's just plain.

The End

# First Glance

*Dalton Lauderback*
*Riverdale High School, Grade 10*

Pacing back and forth,
Heart pounding in my chest;
Overwhelmed by emotion,
I had never felt like this.

Bowing my head,
I whispered a prayer;
Then opened my eyes,
To see them standing there.

Mind racing with thoughts,
Eyes flooding with tears;
And with that first glance,
Fled all my fears.

My little brothers and sisters,
I greeted with, "Ya tee-bya lyu-blyu."
Those three little words,
Translated, "I love you."

Giving all three a hug,
And looking around;
My family of seven,
All safe and sound.

We all were together,
In perfect harmony;
On that, the best day of my life,
God had truly blessed me.

# The Only Daddy I Know

*Arin Anderson*
*Eagleville School, Grade 12*

When I was twelve years old, barely in fifth grade, I found out something that really changed my life. I remember walking in my house right after getting off the bus. My mom walked into the living room and asked to speak to me. I followed her through her bedroom into the bathroom. She closed both doors and then asked me to sit down. At first I was scared that I was in trouble until I heard "You know I love you…" My mom continued to tell me that my daddy wasn't my biological father. She was scared that someone else would tell me and I would get mad at her for not telling me before then. After hearing the news I wanted to cry, but I'm not sure if it was because I was sad or not. I think I was scared because I wasn't expecting it, but I guess no fifth grade child ever expects to be told something like that.

My mom told me that she and my biological father planned to have me when they were seventeen years old. He was there for her through her whole pregnancy. But when it came time for my birth he left and she never saw him again. So my Daddy is the only father figure that I have ever known, besides my uncle Mike.

When I was younger, around four or five, I was always afraid of my Dad. I was afraid of him because he was never home and he and my mom would always fight every time that they were around each other. But as I got older, I began to realize how much I did care for him and how great it was to have a daddy like him in my life.

I now respect my daddy more than I ever have, because he has been there for me when I know that he didn't have to be. I'm so glad that my daddy took me in as his own child. I strongly believe that anyone can be a father to a child but it takes a true man to step up to the plate and be a child's daddy. In the end, the child will have so much respect for the person who was there for them when they know that he chose to be.

# Best Friends Forever

*Julia Henderson*
*Smyrna Primary School, Grade 5*

Beautiful
Easy to spot
Sweet enough to eat
There for you

Fun to talk to
Ready to listen
Intelligent
Everlasting friendship
Numerous ideas
Destined to be by your side
Since third grade

From town to town
Okay to be yourself
Renovations not needed
Everyone is different
Very patient
Endless laughter
Ready to go

**Friendship** • *Alyssa Dawson* • *Barfield Elementary School, Grade 2*

# Family

*Adrian Garcia*
*Roy Waldron Elementary School, Grade 4*

I think family means happy times.  All families have to love each other and respect each other but always think about your family first. Families always protect you no matter what. What I love about my family is that they stick up for me and I will always love my family.


# A Special Memory

*Christian Puig*
*Roy Waldron Elementary School, Grade 5*

I will never forget the time I had a special memory.
It all started on a beautiful Saturday in Puerto Rico.
I went to Grandpa's house to eat.  I was very hungry.
Then I ate a juicy steak and crispy French fries with my Grandpa.
I asked him if he had a memory book.
He said, "Yes." I asked him if I could see it.
He said, "Yes," again.  He took out an enormous book.
We looked at every photo.
And, there was a very special photo.
Do you know why it was so special?
We were all together in that photo:
Mí papí, mí mamí, mí hermano, mí hermana,
Mí tío, mí tía, mí abuela, mí abuelo, and mí!
That's why it's a special memory for me.

# Sidney

*Halee Gregory*
*Eagleville School, Grade 11*

Can you truly realize how brothers and sisters influence our lives? How can something born into this world, so precious and delicate, become something so important? Have we ever taken this into consideration?

On the day my sister Sidney came into this world, I knew she would cause a major change in my life. However, I did not consider how much of a change at that time. Mostly every other older brother or sister in this world celebrates the birth of a newborn sibling. Oddly, I was jealous! However, I was thankful that she was healthy and beautiful but I wasn't prepared to have someone like her around. How would life be from now on? Scared and inexperienced, I accepted her as my baby sister and accepted the fact that challenges were to come.

Now, five years later, I am so thankful to have her in my life and could not imagine it without her. She makes me feel strong, and I know I will be there for her whenever she needs me. As I watch her grow, I want to be someone she can look up to and trust. A younger sibling follows in the footsteps of the older and desires to grow up just like her big brothers or sister. Without me as influences in her life, how will she grow up? Without them as an influence in my life, how would I be different? I have thought of these questions, and I know my life would change, probably for the worse, if it were not for her. She gives me the strength and energy each and every day to overcome and make decisions in life. Now I can sit back and think, how could I have ever been jealous of something as special as Sidney, my little sister?

# Family

*Ginn Mercado*
*Roy Waldron Elementary School, Grade 5*

Family means a lot to me.
Family means a life to me.
Family means a home to me.
Family means people care about me.
Family means happiness and joy.
I know that I can always count on my family to protect me.
I always trust in them.

# A Special Holiday for a Special Person

*Engy Tawfik*
*Roy Waldron Elementary School, Grade 5*

Have you ever wanted to do something for your mom but you didn't know how? Well, I did, and it was on Mother's Day. Mother's Day is a very important day for my family. We all get to give our mothers something very special. Once on Mother's Day, I tried to give my mom something GREAT. It was a silver diamond ring. I really thought that it would be a fabulous present, and it was. The problem was that the ring cost twenty dollars and I had fifteen dollars. I had to save five more dollars. I took out trash; I cleaned my room and made it extra shiny. At last, I had five more dollars. I went back to the store and bought the silver diamond ring. I had to keep it safe until Mother's Day came. I didn't have to wait very long because Mother's Day finally arrived.

"Happy Mother's Day! Happy Mother's Day, Mom! I worked so hard to get this present for you, and I hope you like it."

"WOW! That's really something. Thanks, Engy, it is really beautiful."

"I hope you like it," I said.

"I sure do," my mom said. "Thanks a lot, Engy."

"You are definitely welcome!"


# Memories of My Friend

*Laura Kulp*
*Siegel Middle School, Grade 8*

Remembering when we used to play
Everlasting
Memories flood my mind.
Thinking about the times we spent together
Always carefree,
Endlessly blithesome,
Jubilant in our daydreams.
Every time I dwell upon the past
My heart recalls what memories I have cultivated in my short life.
Lingering on the most pleasant,
Jumbling the undesirable,
Sorting through every last memory and
Arranging them by their amiability,
Knee-deep in my thoughts,
Stopping only to
Briefly pause on the unforgettable experiences.
Journeys, it seems, can be found in every memory.
Memories are all that I have left of my friend.

## My Mother Stella

*Jeanine Uwineza*
*Roy Waldron Elementary School, Grade 5*

My mom is the nicest person you could ever meet, and she is beautiful and nice. She is great. Her hair is brown and black. She makes me smile all the time. I look at her and it is like I'm looking at an angel. I feel wonderful around her. She is a good mother. She likes to shop. She doesn't work. She spoils my brother and me. She likes to look good. She wears boots. She likes going places. She likes having fun. I love her. She is the best. I hope that I am just like her when I grow up.


## My Grandma

*Gabriel Trotter*
*Walter Hill Elementary School, Grade 2*

My grandma is very special to me. She lives in Mississippi. I visit her during the summer. She is a great cook. She has special recipes. I love her very much. She bakes me sweet potato pies and cakes. Last summer we went to Red Lobster. We ate shrimp and crab legs. Seafood is our favorite. She will visit on Thanksgiving. I can't wait!


## To Daddy

*Isaac Gonzalez*
*Roy Waldron Elementary School, Grade 5*

Dear Daddy,

I have a good day every day. I miss you so much. When are you going to come back, Dad? Mom is happy too, but sometimes sad because you are not here. I want to know if you are working hard at your job so you can come back home to be with me. I don't have anyone to play with because Mom is working all week.

Love,
Isaac


## My Grandpa

*Kobe Philalom*
*Blackman Elementary School, Grade 4*

I have a blind grandpa. I call him Papa for short. He is my mother's dad. He lives in a nursing home in Chattanooga. We try to visit him as often as we can. Anytime we visit him, he is happy to see us. I sometimes feel sad for him. I hope someday he'll be able to see me play sports, because Papa loves sports.

# Hope

*Summer Mullins*
*Walter Hill Elementary School, Grade 3*

Hope is my best friend.
She is funny.
We play together.
We live close to each other.
We knew each other in kindergarten.
We swing on the tire swing together.
I like to play with Hope.
We spend the night together.
We are going to be best friends forever.


# My Special Weekend with Gran

*Autumn Martin*
*Blackman Elementary School, Grade 4*

About a month after school started my grandmother invited me to come to her house for the weekend. It was just me; my brothers were not invited. I also got to get out of school early and ride in my uncle's truck. This was just a granddaughter and Gran weekend.

At Gran's house, I got to make a quilt cloth ball. I wanted to make one for my little brother because he always plays with mine. Here are the steps to make a quilted cloth ball:

Get fabric and stuffing.
Cut the fabric.
Sew the fabric together but with a little hole.
Stuff cloth ball with stuffing.
Sew the little hole together.
Play with ball.

The last day we went to Dollywood. We rode cool rides. We rode a ride called the Dizzy Disc. My grandmother never rides Dizzy Disc, but she did this time. We saw one cool show. We went into a few stores. We saw some puzzles, books, necklaces and refrigerator magnets. We had a good time together.

It was fun at my Gran's that weekend and I had a great time. I would like to go to my grandmother's again by myself. I enjoyed my special weekend at Gran's.

# Chapter Three

# Life's Goals

## My Time
*Katie Arnette*
*Central Middle School, Grade 8*

perplexed yet aware
wonder where I stand in life
waiting for my time


## I Can
*Khadijah Carter*
*Smyrna West Alternative School, Grade 9*

I can succeed
I always knew I could
If only they knew how good I was.
I used to think I had nothing to offer
But now I know I can only prosper.
You might think that I'm just chasing a dream
But I really can be anything!


## Traveled Destinations
*Allison Williams*
*Siegel High School, Grade 12*

Looking back on years past,
I'm able to see how blessed I've been.

The hand I've been dealt is better than many,
Though I sometimes fail to see its hidden splendor.

From childhood play dates to elementary recess,
Middle School transitions to high school acceptance.

Tears have been shed and laughter shared,
Gaining new friends and learning new skills.

What lies ahead of me is still a mystery,
My future plans are still unclear.

Still a world of opportunity awaits a willing heart,
The excitement of what's ahead makes each day worth discovering.

# Dreaming

*Keji Oladinni*
*LaVergne Lake Elementary School, Grade 5*

People always say, "I have my head in the clouds."
If that is true, I dream big, and don't plan on coming down.

Meeting famous people or having lots of fun,
Playing soccer with Mia Hamm or marrying David Beckham's son.

Becoming a famous musician or even meeting one,
Or maybe becoming a comedian; if only I had a pun.

I hope to be a doctor, looking at organs and big brains,
How about a meteorologist, so I'll know when it rains?

Being a caterer would be cool, to eat all of the food,
I'd never be a judge, all big, mean, and rude.

If being a lawyer would put me in a Porsche,
Then being a cowboy would get me a horse.

No matter what I am, I am still me,
No matter where I am, my head is still in a tree.

People always say, "I have my head in the clouds."
If that is true, I dream big, and don't plan on coming down.


# College

*Trent Gibson*
*Blackman Elementary School, Grade 3*

Certain to study hard
Opportunity to play sports
Learn every day
Laugh with friends
Exciting place
Grow a lot
End each day happy

# Everything I Want to Be

*Jeremy Walls*
*Smyrna Primary School, Grade 4*

I can be anything I want to be!
I just have to try.
I can be a dolphin trainer
Teaching dolphins how to fly!

I can be a racecar driver
Zooming fast on a track!
I would win every race
Get a trophy and a golden Cadillac!

I can be a Chucky Cheese Man!
I'd give out prizes every day!
The kids would need lots of tickets.
They would say, "Hooray!"

I could be an artist!
I'd teach kids how to draw.
I'd let them play with clay
And make a present for their grandma!

I could be a skydiver!
I'd jump out of a plane!
I'd see little, tiny buildings.
I'd like to land in Spain!

These are all the things that I could be
But I think I'll just be JEREMY!!


# My Future

*Alexis Hibdon*
*Lascassas Elementary School, Grade 4*

When I grow up and get out of high school, I want to go to college to be a surgeon. I think it would be the best feeling to be able to save a life!

My mom is an RN, and my sister wants to be a pediatrician. My little sister tells everyone she wants to be just like me. Therefore, I want to show her that she can be anything she wants to be if she just works for it.

When I become a surgeon, I want my mema and pa to come and live with me. They have helped my family a lot. I also would like to have a husband and family so I can watch them grow up and know they are mine.

## No One Told Me

*Cora Frye*
*Siegel High School, Grade 12*

No one told me it was coming this quickly.
Was it supposed to be this soon?
As expected as the waning of the moon,
It is as surprising as the first flowers after frost.
So many ends wrapped in an even bigger beginning,
Am I really ready for this?
Truly ready to walk across that stage and end a journey?
To adopt a new goal, a new place to work toward?
My head knows it must let go,
That all must pass through this seemingly endless barrage of hugs and tears,
All must pass through in order to start that short walk to an outstretched hand holding that coveted piece of paper.
My new life can now start, and I can begin to search for the Father's calling.
But still my heart reels,
No one told me it was coming this soon.

**Destination of Life** • *Takanori Yashimoto* • *Christiana Middle School, Grade 7*

## A Poem
*Jessica Rochester*
*Siegel Middle School, Grade 8*

       I don't understand….
Why some girls have to start unnecessary drama,
Why friends fade after a long time,
Why people take the precious lives of others.

       But most of all…
Why when you hear a certain song you feel so many mixed emotions,
Why people say things they don't truly mean,
Why people just don't care anymore.

       What I understand most is….
Why adults emphasize kids working hard in school so much,
Why we should work tremendously hard for what we want,
Why we are pushed to follow our dreams when we are young.


## My Dreams
*Adela Felicianos-Knies*
*Blackman Elementary School, Grade 2*

Hi, I had a dream. In my dream, I was an artist painting beautiful pictures. I also dreamed I was a musician playing beautiful music on a stage. That's my dream.


## My Dream
*Ashley Minnich*
*Lascassas Elementary School, Grade 3*

My dream is to be a teacher. I hope I become one. When I grow up, I'm going to take the class to be a teacher. I really wish my dream comes true. I want to teach at an elementary school. I want to teach little kids because they are easier to teach, and I won't have to teach times, division, and algebra. I could teach middle or high school, but I would rather teach little kids.


## How to Be a Good Citizen
*Cameron Henderson*
*Smyrna Primary School, Grade 2*

You can recycle. You can help others. You can help your community. You can pick up trash. You can help animals. That's how to be a good citizen.

## Policeman
*Kaleb Garrett*
*Lascassas Elementary School, Grade 3*

My dream is to be a policeman, because they help the world. They put bad people in jail for taking drugs and drinking and driving. Maybe I will be one one day.


## I Am
*Rachel Ivey*
*Blackman Elementary School, Grade 3*

I am a kind, artistic girl.
I wonder if I will get to be an artist.
I hear a paintbrush painting a glamorous picture.
I see a painting that I inspire.
I want someone to make a picture I love.
I am a kind, artistic girl.

I pretend to be an artist.
I feel paint glimmering on my fingertips.
I touch a painting.
I worry if someone doesn't like my paintings.
I cry if people hate me.
I am a kind, artistic girl

I understand when you need help.
I say you can count on me if you need art tips.
I dream of being in an art museum.
I hope to be an artist.
I am a kind, artistic girl.


## Poem
*Reginald Patterson*
*Oakland High School, Grade 12*

Many people have destinations,
But do not know which way to go.
Some people choose the right path;
Other people choose the immoral road.

You make your own destiny,
But you cannot choose your own fate.
You will meet the destination you seek
Depending on which road you take.

# I Am

*Summer Beauvais*
*Blackman Elementary School, Grade 3*

I am a smart, funny girl.
I wonder if I am ever going to become a scientist.
I hear me shouting, "Hurray!"
I see me going to college.
I want a degree to be a nurse.
I am a smart, funny girl.

I pretend to be a nurse.
I feel proud.
I touch the sky.
I worry when one of my family members is in the hospital.
I cry when someone or something passes away.
I am a smart, funny girl.

I understand people.
I say God will always be with me.
I dream that I have four dogs.
I try to make good grades.
I hope I can do better in school.
I am a smart, funny girl.


# The Journey

*Drew Thompson*
*Oakland High School, Grade 12*

Runners. Some wake up early in the morning while others prefer the night. For many, it is a grueling task, yet they repeat the ritual the very next day. They wander aimlessly through the streets, trails, and countryside only to end up where they began. Others ask where they are going. Runners will tell them that it is not the destination, it is the journey that counts.

## Indefinite Destination

*Shelbi Miller*
*Stewarts Creek Middle School, Grade 7*

My destination, I don't know.
Where shall I stop?
Where will I go?
There's no easy way to plan your future.
Predicting that would be peculiar.
It's hard to see things crystal clear.
Read on a little further
And my destination you will hear.
There is one thing I've learned
(Even though you might not believe me.)
Not everything you learn is going to be all that easy.
But if you have faith and believe,
There won't be anything you can't achieve.
My destination is where I will stop
A doctor, a nurse, or maybe even a cop.
There's no telling what I will see.
So until then, I will be the best person I can be.


## Live for the Journey

*Brandon Messick*
*Oakland High School, Grade 12*

To have arrived somewhere
Is said to be the end of a journey.
The destination is reached,
But tomorrow another journey will ensue
With a new destination,
And the process will continue until the end of time.
So instead of looking ahead of the destination,
Maybe we should look at the journey.
This is where the true memories are made,
Not the ones captured on film, no
These are the memories captured in our minds.
These that will never yellow nor tear;
These that last forever until the end.
So don't stress over a destination,
Or you'll be stressing forever;
Because life's a journey
And how we live our journey
Will determine our destination.

# Dirt Bike Rider

*Noah Walters*
*Eagleville School, Grade 3*

One of my goals is to become a professional dirt bike rider. I am trying to get better but my older brother is better than I am. I practice every day on my track, but I can't get this one double right. I try so hard, but I don't gas it hard enough. My dad was a really good rider, but he quit. When I grow up I want to be like Ricky Carmichael. One day, I'm going to be like my brother, and some day I am going to go to the X-games!


# My Dream

*Neil Watson*
*Stewarts Creek Middle School, Grade 7*

My dream is to go near and far
Playing as a basketball star,
Shooting hoops on all of the teams,
But it won't be as easy as it seems.
I'll have to practice every day,
With few breaks along the way.
But, I'll have to have good grades in school,
And not act like I'm "too cool"
So if I do this, it'll be fun.
But I will have to take each day one by one.


# Policeman

*Abby Raines*
*Wilson Elementary School, Kindergarten*

I want to be a policeman. If there is a fire, I will go to the house and help them get out. If someone is being mean, I will take them to jail. When my family is asleep and there is a fire, I will come get them out. If the firefighters need help, I will help them.


# My Destination in Life

*Jordyn Carter*
*Blackman Elementary School, Grade 1*

My destination in life is to be a doctor and help others.

## My Destination in Life

*Matthew Medlin*
*Blackman Elementary School, Grade 1*

I am destined to be a Marine.


## My Dream

*Miller Raybon*
*Cedar Grove Elementary School, Grade 3*

When I grow up, I want to be an architect. I want to design buildings, furniture, and toys. I like to design things. My favorite thing is to build with legos. My mom and I like to watch designing shows on HGTV. Since I watch them, my dad and I designed a table and built it. We built it for designing legos. My dad is a builder, so I learned a lot from him.


## Believe

*Kimi Warren*
*Stewarts Creek Middle School, Grade 6*

Dreams can be sports cars.
Dreams can be jobs or a shining trip to the stars.
No matter who you are, your dreams can come true if you just believe.
Don't mope and don't slope.
Believe
Believe not only for you but for the man without a home, or
The girl who begs for food in the streets of Rome.
For you can make a difference to them.
When you wish you can be who you want to be.
You can be Bill Gates or president
Just believe


## My Goals for the Future

*Hannah Seifert*
*LaVergne Lake Elementary School, Grade 4*

My goal in the future is to make superb grades through middle school, graduate high school, and then get an athletic scholarship to Princeton. Once I'm a grown-up, I hope to find the right guy for me and get a job I love. Then, just like my mom and dad, have kids that I will cherish with all my heart. I hope they'll feel the same way, too. That is the future that I want.

## I Hope to Be in the Army

*Noah Barrett*
*Lascassas Elementary School, Grade 3*

One day I would like to join the Army. I think you go to this certain school, and do a bunch of training until you get fully trained. Then you go to the Army camp where you do a bunch of stuff like target practic and drop from helicopters. It just seems very fun, and I love my country and my family.

## What I Want to Be When I Grow Up

*Amber Sellers*
*Lascassas Elementary School, Grade 3*

My name is Amber. I am nine years old. When I grow up I would like to be a vet that helps sick animals and pets. I want to be a vet because I love pets and animals. Plus, I like science. My favorite kinds of animals are wild animals and pet animals. My favorite kind of wild animals are cheetahs, leopards, wolves, jaguars, panthers, and zebras. My favorite kinds of pet animals are yorkies, Dalmatians, and poodles. That is what I want to be when I grow up.

**Destinations** • *Bethany Zuniga* • *Rockvale Middle School, Grade 6*

## My Hopes and Dreams

*Brenna Cronk*
*Cedar Grove Elementary School, Grade 3*

I've always dreamed about going to college and becoming a doctor. I want to become a doctor because I like to help people and help sick people to make them feel better and give them a flu shot so they don't get sick. I would also like to be a doctor to help deliver babies. I would like to learn how to do surgery on people so if I do have to do surgery on someone I don't want to mess up and get fired. After I get a career and everything, I'm going to get married and take really good care of my kids. Finally, we will have one happy family and it will be great!

## My Dreams and Wishes

*Branden Tok*
*Cedar Grove Elementary School, Grade 3*

Branden
Clever, comical, hardworker, respectful.
Son of Tina and Dara.
Lover of video games, TV, and animals.
Who wishes to be the president of the U.S.A.
Who dreams of being a soccer player.
Who wants to jump off the Empire State Building and Statue of Liberty.
Who wonders how many frogs there are.
Who is afraid of Michael Jackson.
Who likes ramen noodles.
Who loves his family.
Who plans to be a doctor.
Tok

# What It Means to Be an African American

*Ashley Colemon*
*Thurman Francis Arts Academy, Grade 8*

Being an African American goes deeper than how much money you have or the neighborhood in which you live. To be an African American means that we are triumphant. We know our ancestors worked for the many opportunities we have today. We are accomplishing feats that were impossible only a few decades ago. For example, I'm proud that we now have the first African American president-elect of the United States, and the first appointed African American female to become Secretary of State. I'm part of history!

Additionally, I think of another word: audacity. We have the valor to speak out, even when all the odds are against us. We persevere and keep working until goals have been achieved. We have the faith to believe, even though darkness may loom around the corner. To me, being an African American means having the victory of overcoming a rough past, the courage to be strong in tough situations, and the audacity to have hope toward a brighter day.

# Toys for Tots

*Katy Hobart*
*Cedar Grove Elementary School, Grade 4*

When I grow up I want to be a Toys for Tots person. That is a person who lets people give away just a little bit of their clothes, food, blankets, wigs, and toys for people who are poor and don't have a home. I want to help them.

# Destinations

*Sarah Swinford*
*Thurman Francis Arts Academy, Grade 6*

**D**ream
**E**xiting
**S**pecial
**T**omorrow
**I**maginative
**N**ever give up
**A**dventurous
**T**oday
**I**nventive
**O**riginal
**N**ew
**S**omeday!!!!

# My Destination, Not Here

*Siori Koerner*
*Christiana Middle School, Grade 7*

Between the complications of life,
The tangled strings of what makes me "me"
A question lingers in the back of my mind
Of where I am supposed to be.

Do I really belong
In the suburb of where I am?
Or am I a nothing that belongs nowhere?
Is this just one of life's scams?

In this shallow world,
The trends will come and go.
But does any of it matter when you're totally alone?
Oh, where do I belong?

What is my final destination?
Where is it and how can I get there?
Because there's one thing I am certain about,
It surely isn't here.

# My Destination . . .Goal!

*Savannah Stevens*
*Thurman Francis Arts Academy, Grade 6*

I went to the soccer field on Friday night.
It was a battle, it was a soccer fight.
We played with all our might.
I scored my goal on that cold night.
My goal is to try my best.
And not to worry about the rest.
If I can accomplish that, it would be really great.
I hope to do my best, I hope others will appreciate.

# Sea of Life

*Samantha Blankenship*
*Stewarts Creek Middle School, Grade 6*

The current is demanding for me to choose
I want the winning way, not the way I'll lose.

"Row," says my heart
"Wait," says my brain
My heart knows where to go, but my brain wants to think.

I am frozen in place
Do I want a dangerous life
Or one that's safe?

The Sea of Life can take everything from you,
But in the long run it gives everything back and more, too.

Take the way your heart wants you to go
Did you take the right path?
You soon will know!

# Will I Take the Right Road?

*Kaia Lyons*
*Thurman Francis Arts Academy, Grade 6*

As a child, I've dreamed of my life in the future. I know that there are good paths and bad paths, cliffs and dead ends, rewards and punishable consequences. But aside from all those, in a secluded area, is the road less traveled. I've heard of it before, and I can't wait to go, but I first must find it. What is popular isn't always right, and what is wrong is not always popular. If I graduate with accomplished, smart, wise seniors who have an idea of what their lives should be, then that's not only what is right but also what is popular.

No matter what happens, I want to be on the right path, and I don't want to do the wrong things. I don't want to smoke or drink or mess up my life permanently in any way. And to do that, I no longer know for sure whether the road less traveled is really the right road. But I will pray, hope, trust, and believe that God will help me choose which road to take.

# I Elect to Be Drug Free

*Peyton Manus*
*Smyrna Primary School, Grade 4*

My name is Peyton Manus. I'm only ten years old but I want to tell you something. I've already elected to be drug free. If people say, "Here take this, it'll make you feel better."

I'll say, "No way, because I'm drug free and drug free means I'll never do drugs as long as I live. So, I'm not going to take that harmful thing in your hand."

If they say, "You're a chicken." Then I'll walk away and not say a word, because I'm a good role model and good role models don't take drugs. If anybody, and I mean anybody, gives you something dangerous or something you don't know what somebody is giving you, don't take it. Just throw it away or give it to the teacher.

# My Dream Is to Fly

*Dakota Leigh Frech*
*Blackman Elementary School, Grade 5*

My dream is to fly, to fly
High in the sky,
Dreaming about kites
And a nice life.
I want to fly high
In the sky like a butterfly
With the lovely fragrance
Of steaming pie
For me, for you, and
For Libby Lou.
Let's fly high in the
Sky and have a
Wonderful time.
So my dream is to
Fly, to fly high in the sky.

## If I Were President

*Griffin Kepfer*
*Barfield Elementary School, Grade 2*

If I were president, I would achieve goals and lower taxes to $1 and $1.50.  I will help people be good citizens. If I ever become president of the United States of America, I promise to do my best.  I will help the United States of America.


## The Dream

*Jacob Wilkinson*
*Rock Springs Elementary School, Grade 5*

Piled into bed,
Pillow on my head,
It came with steam,
A wonderful dream.
I look everywhere,
I saw a white hare.
It was snowing,
And the beauty, well it was glowing.
After awakening, I have another one,
And this one was quite fun.
Dragons and dungeons, wizards as well,
But soon I awoke, after a magical spell.
Soon I went back to slumbering,
As well as wondering,
What my next dream would be,
But I soon would see,
With pirates, this one was cool,
Floating over a water pool.
Finally the alarms ring,
Woke me up from a magical spring.
I thought of what I'd seen,
Wondering what they all did mean.
But then I figured this:
Whatever they may be,
Dreams make me, me.


## I Can Be Drug Free!

*Tristin Cox*
*Smyrna Primary School, Grade 2*

I know how to be drug-free!  If someone gave me a drug, I would throw it down.  I don't like drugs.  They are bad for you.  I want to be drug-free!

# The Bus

*Elizabeth VanMeter*
*Eagleville School, Grade 9*

When I look back on it today I ask myself, "Why did I want to ride the bus so badly?" Sure it is fun, because you get to talk to your friends, but it gets kind of hectic sometimes and the place it takes you is not very fun to go to. So, why did I want to ride the bus so badly? Could it have been because I was ready to get out of the house and grow up, or was it that I wanted to explore new things?

When I was four years old, I used to always go out on the front porch and wait for the big, bright yellow school bus to go by. Every afternoon I would go outside and wait for it to go by. I couldn't wait to see it! This was my favorite time of the day. I would put on my backpack my mom had gotten for me and go outside and pretend I was going to get on that school bus. I knew it wouldn't be long before I was able to ride it, but it seemed like it was taking forever.

When it did go by in the afternoons, I could see all of the kids that were on it. They all looked different. Some were smiling and some frowning, but I didn't care because I knew I would be one of the ones smiling. Sometimes she even honked her horn, especially if I was still outside when she came back through and the bus was empty. I loved it whenever she would honk her horn, because I loved the noise and it made me feel like I was someone on the bus, and that it noticed me.

Finally, when I started kindergarten I got my chance to ride the bus. I was so excited! I hurt my mom's feelings though, because I walked down the driveway, got on the bus, and never looked back.

"Why I wanted to ride the bus?" I still don't know; I guess it's because I wanted to get out of the house. I was ready to go my own way and start my own life and begin fulfilling my dreams.

# My Destination

*Breanna Urdiera*
*Smyrna West Alternative School, Grade 7*

Where am I heading to?
Am I on the right road?
Will I succeed in life?
People tell me I could do better…
Can I?

# I Can't Believe This

*Jessica Helton*
*Eagleville School, Grade 11*

The month of August was rolling around and the weather began to cool down. Unbeknownst to me as of late, school, started around this time of the year as well. For the last eight years, I had been receiving my education via a computer. No teachers, no students, just me and myself. For those last years, I had become extremely socially awkward

So, this was my first day of school. Real school. This was not a simulated classroom of a room full of imaginary students. This was the real deal. The whole situation seemed so surreal. This was surreal in my perspective anyways.

I was as lost as a puppy dog in the middle of the woods. I still lived in my little bubble and this did not work out well at all at first. I walked around so ungainly; I was still not used to walking around much. Thousands of thoughts ran through my head. One of the thoughts was, "Is this the right classroom? Will the teacher dislike me? What do you do in class? What does a teacher look like?"

I began panicking. I felt like crying in the bathroom until 2:45, which was the time TV shows had said school usually was out. On my first day, I had not obtained a single friend. This made me feel extremely lonely. I wanted to go home. I wanted to go back to that computer screen, and imaginary friends and act like that was normal. However, I knew I could not go back to that. I signed my soul away to the public school system. I wasn't leaving for another five years, sadly.

After a while, I began to notice everyone walking in one general direction, towards the gym. Everyone seemed happy and excited. I felt so out of place because of this. I walked up the bleachers and took my seat. Everyone was cheering. Happy emotions were everywhere, and I still felt out of place. After the pep rally, I made my way to the car lot. I lost my balance and fell down at least five bleachers. It happened so quickly. I was so embarrassed. However, people began to talk to me. It made me feel like things were starting to go my way. I think I made friends.


# I'm a Vet!

*Hanna E. Dunn*
*Stewartsboro Elementary School, Grade 3*

Someday I will be a veterinarian. All I have to do is get over my fear of dogs…well, big dogs. Then when I am over my fear of dogs, I will make the perfect vet. At least, that is what I think. I am learning karate right now in third grade. I will soon have my black belt. No dog will dare to bite me then!

When I am in college and when I get a job, I won't be scared of dogs. If one bites me, I probably won't even notice. Maybe I need to stop thinking about dog bites.

Someday I will reach my destination of becoming a veterinarian and will become the best vet Murfreesboro has ever seen!!

## Just Me

*Adrion Lee*
*Smyrna West Alternative School, Grade 9*

> One window is all I need
> To find a girl who understands me.
> And just maybe
> Friends we could be.
> One window is all I need
> To see what God has in store for me.
> To open up and be free
> So that people could get to know
> Just me.

## I Want to Be a Singer

*Kalysta Gonzalez*
*Stewartsboro Elementary School, Grade 3*

When I grow up, I want to be a singer. Then, I can continue to write my own songs. When I have finished writing a new song, I love to sing it in my room. I would be really happy to be a singer. People could then hear my thoughts through my songs. Singing is my hobby now but maybe my destination is to be a famous, wealthy singer and song writer.

**Everyone Wants to Be in the Spotlight** • *Justin Henderson* • *Oakland High School, Grade 12*

# Journey of Me

*Kaley Humphrey*
*Siegel High School, Grade 11*

I knew singing in the car on my way to the zoo.
I knew bear hugs, holding hands, and kisses, too.
I knew warm sunshine beaming down on my head,
And Eskimo kisses as I climbed into bed.
Then I heard words that I had not known,
And angry faces quickly hung up the phone.
Then it seems she was gone in a flash, in a blink.
With no one to hear them, I washed tears down the sink.
So many times when she wasn't there,
To hug me, to hold me, or just brush my hair.
But then she was back and you know what they say,
The longer they left you, the longer they'll stay.
Since she had been gone for a lifetime it seemed,
I knew she'd not leave me, so beside her I beamed.
The girl became grown and without much delay,
Hours of homework traded for hours of play.
It seems two personalities dwell within me,
With one on the forefront, the second secedes.
One strong and on fire, never caught unaware,
One pensive and peaceful, but beneath all is scared.
But neither will lose and neither will win,
For where I am going is where I have been.
I will find a balance to me and this world,
And then I'll help others with their fearful girl.
No one should worry and no one should pain,
Because rainbows shine only after the rain.
So that's where I'm headed and that's where I've been.
What I haven't told you, you'll have to fill in.
And who knows what I'll go through to eventually be
The person I'll find on this journey of me.

# Decision 2008

*Brian Allen*
*Siegel High School, Grade 10*

Our once great nation is falling apart before our eyes
Debates and promises are filled with decisiveness and lies
But now, it's time for a decision...Decision 2008,
As we watch both of the candidates aggressively debate.

We are a country divided; emotions are running high,
So we look to these two candidates to find what went awry.
Wall Street, home foreclosures, rising gas prices,
All these problems are leading to an economic crisis.

Americans across the land have raised the question,
Which of the candidates will help us avoid a great depression?
This election is a turning point in American history.
The outcome has become an intriguing mystery.

Who can create more jobs and a better health care plan?
Which of the candidates can fix what George Bush began?
Whom can we expect to finally end the war in Iraq?
And who will be able to prevent a possible terrorist attack?

We are all witness to an historic election,
And voters must make an informed selection.
McCain and Palin...dumb and dumber...
And, of course, the secretary of state: Joe Plumber.


# Field of Dreams

*Tucker Morgan*
*Wilson Elementary School, Grade 1*

　　　　When I grow up, I want to be a baseball player. I will hit home runs for my team. When I get too old to play baseball, I want to create baseball games. The new game will be high tech and will be played by all game devices. Then when I am really old, I will become a baseball coach. This will help me keep my baseball dreams alive.


# When I Grow Up

*Christian Martinez*
*Blackman Elementary School, Grade 2*

　　　　When I grow up I want to be an architect. An architect is someone who builds schools and homes. They also draw banks and stores. I want to build a mall. It will be fun being an architect. I learned the word architect when I was just four years old.

## What I Want to Do in the Future

*David Milam*
*Blackman Elementary School, Grade 2*

When I grow up, I want to go to college. Then, I will play college football. I want to be on the Vols team. Next, when I get finished with college, I want to be a hockey player so I can get a lot of money. Last, I want to be a dad and have two kids named Ben and Zack. I will get a wife, too. I will be a grandpa. Then I will retire.

## A Childhood Craft

*Rebekah Harris*
*Siegel High School, Grade 12*

As a little girl I loved those paper chains.
I tried to make each chain so colorful and long.
Stretching them across the wall, each having its own lane,
I made sure every link sang a different song.

Life is much like this childhood craft,
Each chain representing a different person
       And each link a different stage;
Connecting people and places with whom I have laughed,
All through my life, at every age.

My life is made up of all these moments and possibilities
Making me who I am today
And inspiring me to become something I desire to be.

Although I am unsure what the future will bring,
I can look at my parents' chains they have made
And learn from the lessons they were taught to sing,
Incorporating them into the path I hope to someday lay.

With support and encouragement from my family and friends,
I will be able to achieve my dream of making life less to bear.
Touching those children in bends,
Completing my chain and connecting it to theirs.

# The End

*Courtney Wright*
*Christiana Middle School, Grade 8*

It's waiting for you from the day you are born
It shadows your life
It haunts your dreams
It strikes fear in even the bravest of men
It brings tears and sorrows
But also relief and peace
It blackens your thoughts
It forces you to sacrifice what you hold dear
It bestows pain and suffering
It creates lamentations from the depths of your soul
It is your foe
It is your friend
It makes you burn with passionate hatred and revenge
It forces you to realize we aren't "all-knowing"
It is everywhere
Every day
Targeting everyone – rich or poor
And you never know who it will strike next
Death is the final destination

Chapter Four

# Miscellaneous

# What Is Beauty?

*Meagan White*
*Thurman Francis Arts Academy, Grade 8*

What is beauty?
What is it really?
Who is beautiful?
Is anyone really pretty?
In society you have a choice
To be set apart or
To belong.
In the end there is
No right or wrong;
All that matters is
You're standing strong.
To many, beauty
Is what you see–
Hair, eyes, popularity.
To them, beauty
Is make-up and clothes,
But from the heart
Is where real beauty flows.


# Destinations

*Elizabeth Sneed*
*Christiana Middle School, Grade 6*

Destinations, Destinations!
Where shall I go?
Better think fast
Or I will be walking in the snow.
I could go there
Where people are neat
Or maybe there
Where the whole world is sweet.
I don't want to play in the rain
I'd rather ride in a big airplane.
What if I went on a boat,
To save a king across the moat?
Destinations, destinations!
So many places to choose,
But I'd rather be here
Spending time with you.

# First Job

*Brandon Barnes*
*Smyrna High School, Grade 10*

On June 2, 2008, I applied at Little Caesars in Smyrna, Tennessee. The manager called me in for an interview.

I drove down to Little Caesars at about 12:27 P.M. Sweating nervously, I arrived at my destination, and I got out of my truck. I desperately needed to catch some coolness, but all I felt was a warm breeze running through my bald head. I anxiously approached the door, and the manager came up to me and asked me to take a seat. I was so scared. The manager began the interview by asking me numerous questions about customer service and how to dress. With little work experience, I was confused about what to say! After the interview came to an end, he told me to stay close to my phone just in case I got the job, so I would know when to work.

On my way back home from this crazy experience, I was jamming to my rock music and telling myself that everything was going to turn out fine. I pulled into my driveway, shaking, as I pulled the keys out of the ignition. I walked inside my house went straight to my mom and told her about my nerve-racking experience with the interview.

About 6:24 P.M. that day I got the phone call from the manager.

"Brandon, we are giving you a try at Little Caesars. We want you to come in on Wednesday at 12 noon."

Looking back on the interview, I realize things I could have said or should have possibly said, but I guess what I did say was the right thing. I have been at Little Caesars ever since. It is a tough job, but I enjoy every minute of it.


# The Destination Key

*Hayden Marshall*
*Siegel Middle School, Grade 8*

Where have you been,
Where could you go?
If you had the chance to travel,
Would you say no?
Travel by air,
Travel by land?
Travel by truck,
Travel by van?
Where would you go,
What would you see?
You hold in your hand,
The destination key.

## Flowers

*Dylan Ward*
*Rock Springs Elementary School, Grade 2*

Flowers
Red, Green, Blue
Flowers are like rainbows.
Purple, Violet, Orange
Flowers


## The Snake on the Porch

*Catie Moss*
*Homer Pittard Campus School, Grade 1*

Today I saw a snake on my front porch. I was scared and started to cry. My neighbor rang the doorbell. My mom got the hoe. She used a broom, shovel, and a hoe. The hoe killed it.

Mom looked up on the computer to see what kind it was. It may be poisonous. It was a Western Pigmy Rattlesnake. Mom is happy. Yea Mom. I love you, Mom.


## I Am

*Cameron Reed*
*Stewarts Creek Elementary School, Grade 5*

I am an excellent soccer player.
I wonder for whom I will play.
I hear angry screaming, coaches.
I see the full stadium.
I want to break Pele's legendary records.
I am an excellent soccer player.
I pretend to win the World Cup.
I feel the deep emotion in every loss.
I touch the shiny trophy.
I worry we will lose every game.
I cry when my team loses the championship.
I am an excellent soccer player.
I understand you lose sometimes.
I say good game at the end of every game.
I dream to be an all-star.
I try to give one hundred percent each game.
I hope we win.
I am an excellent soccer player.

# Frustration

*Meghan Rice*
*Thurman Francis Arts Academy, Grade 8*

Frustration is like poisonous venom
That flows slowly through your veins
Forcing you to scream and shout with pain
It eats at you until you cannot bear it anymore
And chaos swarms within your perishing corpse
You start to drown in your ocean of thought
And ignore the slightest bit of hope
All the while you're thinking the worst
As you sink to the cold, dark depths of the ocean
Until you see a light at the surface that warms you
A hand reaches down to pull you near
A voice calls from the skies and reminds you
That you are loved and have a friend

# Adventures of a Library Book

*Daniel Kim*
*Siegel Middle School, Grade 8*

There are many exciting tales told, that come from a library book.
But there are not many sagas on the journey the book itself took.

When the barcode with the genre is stuck on the brand new book.
It is like a Medal of Honor for all store-bought books to see.

As it battles many trials it may face the nasty.
The cracks and crevices could be filled with pastries.

It could also face the churning water of a bathtub.
Or be touched by the grubby hands of a small toddler.

It will be loved and caressed by the bookworm and hidden and read in bed.
But thrown aside by the jock –
treated like a block of lead.

A library book experiences many things and goes through many adventures.
Yet its best trait is being able to bring enjoyment to everyone.

# Imagine

*Mazzio Chumney*
*Smyrna High School, Grade 11*

IMAGINE
Being judged so much you become racist yourself.
IMAGINE
Living in a nice neighborhood, with parents that work productive jobs and drive
comfortable vehicles, but the neighbors claim everything we have worked for, comes
from selling drugs.
IMAGINE
Speaking your mind about how you feel and of your beliefs, and your enemies say it's
all a lie.
IMAGINE
If this place we called world were to change for the good.
IMAGINE
Classmates accusing you of cheating because you answered an almost impossible
question correctly.
IMAGINE
If no one was stereotyped, life would be easier.
IMAGINE
Wearing house shoes because you like it with your outfit, and you get called poor and
degrading names when, in fact, you're not.
IMAGINE
Walking in a room and being prejudged.
IMAGINE
Being a gentleman but still looked upon as a "thug."
IMAGINE
being turned down after an interview because supposedly there aren't any openings, but
the truth is they won't hire you because you're black.
IMAGINE
Being talked to like you're stupid just by the way you talk, when you're intelligent.
IMAGINE
Having a job and you're the best at your job.
IMAGINE
Overcoming all these stepping stones, and molding you into a great person, to prove the
people wrong who judged you.
JUST IMAGINE

## Beyond This Beauty

*Kimberlee Cooper*
*Thurman Francis Arts Academy, Grade 8*

Outside, not in,
Always matters where.
Beauty is beauty,
Never quite fair
Either born with it,
Or you just live without.
Some people would do anything to get it,
Without hesitation or a moment of doubt.
This is how we are taught
To think and believe.
Yet, if people could just see,
Our sinful misconception of this thing called beauty.

Inside, not out,
Never matters where.
Beauty comes from the heart,
Not make-up or hair.
Anyone has the potential to be,
Her own special beauty.
Whether blue eyes or brown,
Speckled with gold,
With straight hair or curly,
So frizzy nothing can hold.
Please don't believe
What those before have misconstrued.
It will only demolish
Your beautiful vision of you.

## Fear

*Matt Fowler*
*Thurman Francis Arts Academy, Grade 8*

Fear is a monster that keeps you down,
Keeps you trembling and afraid.
When you try to fly,
It grounds you.
When you try to swim,
It drowns you.
So you stay trembling,
Trembling in a corner.

# The War in Iraq

*Dakota Thigpen*
*Rockvale Middle School, Grade 7*


As the soldiers wake up to a summer's day, they hear the wounded calling out to them,
So they get ready for action.
As the bullets are flying, the wounded are crying.
As the jets fly, so do the heavenly soldiers.
As the soldiers die, they watch upon their family and friends.
As the soldiers run, the angels follow behind.
As the guns and soldiers meet, America sings "America the Beautiful."
As the soldiers say their last farewell they whisper, "Tell my family, I'm not dead, I'm
just answering God's call."
As the eagle flies, the families on Earth and the soldiers in heaven cry.
Rain falls from the Great American sky.


# The People

*Lydia Landrum*
*Rock Springs Middle School, Grade 6*


You've come as far as you can,
Hand in hand,
And to the day you know,
You can feel the pain of the past,
It comes back to you all at once,
A rush of heart-felt horror,
It's an instinct,
An essential lure,
A moment left,
'Til the end,
A moment left,
'Til you win,
We live, we see,
We do, we hate,

Carry the label of you,
Because your name shall have no resemblance,
To the true and honest world, its own horror and all.

# Unionville Rockets

*Samantha Beard*
*Eagleville School, Grade 8*

It was one, cold spring day when I got out of softball practice for the Eagleville Eagles. I then went with my friend Jessie, and we headed to Unionville. When we reached our destination, we were greeted by softballs being thrown through the air. After we were warmed up, we started practicing with the rest of the team. Then Jessie left me to talk to the other girls. I felt very lonely, without her there. After we had stretched, the coaches welcomed us to the team. Then we told them our names and a little bit about ourselves. The coaches' names were Amber, Amanda, and Ashley; we also had a pitching coach named Cora. I was really nervous, because all of the other girls were fantastic. I was just another face on the team to them.

By the third or fourth practice, I had all the girls' names down pat: Nicki, Jessie, Alex, Jamie, Blair, Tayhlor, Caroline, Shelby, and Heather. All the girls were really nice to me; and, by the end of the season, they were like sisters to me.

At the practice before our first tournament Amber told us the roster. Alex –first, Heather –catching, Nicki –pitching, Samantha –third, Jamie shortstop, Tayhlor –second, Caroline –center field, Blair –right field, Jessie –left field, and Shelbie – AH (alternate hitter). Our first tournament was in Manchester. We all met up at the Piggly Wiggly in Unionville. Then we followed them to the field. We were all pumped up and ready to win a game. We were focused and determined. We almost won the first game, but we fell in the last inning. Even though we didn't win a game in that tournament, we still had the courage to go on. About halfway through the season, they changed the roster and put me on first and put Alex as the AH. The rest of the season we didn't win a game, but we were still trying our hardest.

The week before the last tournament we were hit with some bad news. Our pitcher, Nicki, had a knee problem and couldn't play. At that moment we all knew we were doomed, but Coach Amber found a new pitcher. Her name was Chelsea, and she was fantastic. Chelsea had an awesome pitch. She also found a girl named Kaiti. She could hit it over the fence if you asked her to. They were both fantastic players and we were so glad to know that they would be on our team.

At the last tournament we were tied, five to five, with the other team. Then the buzzer rang, signaling the end of the pool play game; then, we played the Murfreesboro team. We ended up beating them two to three. Then in the regular match we lost one and won the other. We came in third in that tournament. It made me so happy to finally win a game, and place third. We all knew that we could do it. We were congratulated with a trophy and a big smile from our parents.

We just had to try our hardest and give it our all. Then after the game, my coach sat us down and congratulated us on our win. Then she told us that she wanted us to move up with them next year. She told us that she would call us when they were going to start practicing again. She told me that I had been a great team leader, and she was looking forward to next year.

Being on the travel team gave me the greatest experience ever. It also welcomed me to a whole knew playing field. It gave me the strength to keep growing as a player and as a team leader. I made many friends and I gained a lot more courage. It also gave me the chance to get the feel of a different kind of softball.

# Destiny
*Mwamini Ndaizeye*
*Siegel High School, Grade 10*

Where is God when you're lonely?
He is right beside you. You may feel lonely, but you are never alone.
Even in the loneliest times, God remains within the range of your voice. You can talk to
Him about anything; God is everywhere…even in places where we feel isolated.
Because he is everywhere, he joins us even when we feel lonely. He never abandons us.
When you feel lonely, use the opportunity to talk with God. Rather than feel miserable
Because you feel alone, enjoy time with Christ. He's still with you.
Thank you Lord, for hanging with me all the time.
Help me to see the people around me who are lonely and let them know they have a
friend.

In Swahili, my native language:

Wapiyesuwakati ukolonely?
Yesu anaweza kuwa upandewako. Lakinaukona seul. Munguanakumbuka juu yasauti
yako unawezakusema kilakitu mungu atakusikia ikopopote.fasiyote tunajisikiya
isolate.kwanini ikofasiyote? Kwasababuyeyenimwezavyote. akunakitukisiy-
owezekanakwake.kilakitukikoraisikwake.
Asante yes kwakunipamudanahii.nisaidienione watu pembeniyanguwenyewakolonely na
waachewenyewe wajuwewakonarafiki.
Nashukurukwawalewenyewalitowaruhusajuuyakuandikakilamojanandotozake-
navinginevyo Asante kwausikilivumwema


# Cystic Fibrosis
*Zoë Gillespie*
*Central Middle School, Grade 7*

CF, part of my life,
part of my world.
I sit in the hospital
waiting and listening.
I look into the eyes
of my sleeping friend
hoping she'll wake soon.
She finally wakes as the
nurse comes in.
We hug and kiss before
she leaves our world.
CF, part of my life,
Part of my world forever.

# I Am

*John Brown*
*Stewarts Creek Elementary School, Grade 5*

I am a Wrestle Mania Freak.
I wonder if it's real.

I hear yelling a lot.

I see blood sometimes, but it's fake.

I want to see more of the program, but I can't stay up late.
I am a Wrestle Mania Freak.

I pretend I'm one of the characters.
I feel strong when I watch it.

I touch and play with my action figures.
I worry if they get hurt sometimes.
I cry when my brother does some moves on me.
I am a Wrestle Mania Freak.

I understand it's not real.
I say I love the show.

I dream that I'm actually fighting.
I try to act like them sometimes.
I hope to be a wrestler one day.
I am a Wrestle Mania Freak.

## Shorthorn

*Holden Ayers*
*Christiana Elementary School, Grade 5*

I showed my shorthorn calf, 9 MM, for the first time at the Expo. My family and I drove to the MTSU cattle barns. First, we unloaded our cows and stuff. Then, we washed and brushed my cows. Then, I got my stick and prepared myself for the show.

Next, I led 9 MM to a waiting area. Here I waited a little while till my number was called. Then, I went into the ring. The judge's helper told me where to go. If you think I was nervous, I really was.

Next, the judge came up to me and asked some questions. What type of feed do you give your calf? How old is your calf? What is the calf's name? I answered all these questions without a problem. I was then asked to lead my calf around the ring; so I did. He judged all the cows and announced the winners. He said who came in first, second, third, and fourth places. I was in fourth.

Then, I led 9 MM out of the ring. From there, I led her back to the barn. I had to prepare for the showmanship part of the show. After awhile, I led 9 MM back to the waiting area again. I waited here until I was called back into the ring.

In the showmanship, you have to show how well you are at showing cattle. Then, I was placed in a spot and was able to get 9 MM ready. From here I just stood and listened to what the judge said.

Finally, the judge announced the winners. Unluckily, I came in last place. I was happy, though, because I knew I had done my best. The experience was good, too, even though I didn't win.


## I Remember

*Gabe Martin*
*Homer Pittard Campus School, Grade 6*

I remember when I got my dog Lucky.
And I remember how we always used to dress him up and chase him around the house.

I remember when my little sister Lily was born.
And I remember how cute she was and how my brother and I tried to get her to play football.

I remember when my little brother Luke was born.
And I also remember how he grew to be curious about everything.

I remember when the Giants won the Super Bowl
And I remember when Eli Manning threw the game-winning touchdown. I was dancing with joy.

I remember my first day of Campus School.
And I remember how nervous I was in kindergarten and how I thought it was scary.

# Callie

*Amanda Harrell*
*Buchanan Elementary School, Grade 6*

One day, my mom and I were going to a Girl Scout meeting at my friend Lindy's house. Her house was on a farm, and they had horses, cats, dogs, and goats. When the meeting was adjourned, Lindy and I went out to play with the animals.

When we came back Ms. Alisha, Lindy's mom, asked me if I wanted to see some kittens, and I shouted, "Yes!" She took me to Lindy's little brother's room, pulled out his Mickey Mouse television, and pointed. I saw five kittens and their mother. I picked up the smallest, palm-sized, calico kitten. She mewed, and huddled close to my chest. Soon, she began to purr. Then my mom called for me, and we left. When we were almost home she asked, "Do you want a kitten?" and, I quickly shouted, "Yes!"

That night, I made a long list for a kitten's basic needs. On the list, I had a litter box, litter, food and water dishes, a collar, tags, and toys. I had saved one-hundred dollars for the essentials.

When I was finished, I ate dinner. While I was eating, my mom said, "There are a lot of cats. Three of Lindy's cats just had kittens. Two litters are old enough to come home tomorrow. I'll take you to Wal-Mart tomorrow before we get your kitten." I stopped her, "I don't want just any kitten; I want the calico kitten. She is fluffy, she purrs, and she is just so cute. If it requires waiting, then I will wait. But, I want her."

"Okay, I will call Ms. Alisha, and tell her. I can still take you to Wal-Mart if you would like."

After I went to bed, I had vivid dreams. Out of nowhere, there was a foul, rotten stench. I heard my mom nagging me, and I looked down. In my hand were trash bags and a litter scooper. I've cleaned litter boxes before, so what was this about? A litter scooper! I forgot to put litter scooper on my list! Almost silently, I crept out of bed, and put litter scooper on the bottom of my list, and went back to sleep. Fortunately, I didn't have any more dreams like that!

In the morning, we went to Wal-Mart. There was nothing exciting there. I got the healthiest food. I also got a big auto feeder, and a large auto waterer. Mom and I found some entertaining toys, too. We also got the rest of the essentials. These items included a litter scooper.

My mom and I waited for six weeks, and finally, I was able to get my kitten. I was so excited my mom said my energy could power a whole city. I didn't care, I was just so happy. We were soon able to go to Lindy's house. When we got there, I saw Lindy and her mom waiting for us. My kitten was squirming, trying to get away from them. She ran straight to me, and mewed. I picked her up, said thank you, and got in the car.

When we got home, I showed the kitten where her litter box, food, and bed were. Next, I wanted to name her. I decided on Callie, because she is a calico. Callie just ran around. Suddenly she began to purr. I thought she liked her new home, and she did.

# A Day at the Bay

*Tyler Thompson*
*Buchanan Elementary School, Grade 6*

It was a day like any other. The sun was out; the water was slowly rippling; the afternoon sun was warming our necks, and the sun was casting a halo of rainbow colors over the lake. It was the perfect day. We were fishing on Percy Priest Lake and not catching anything! We had been driving the boat to different areas for some time and not encountering a single fish.

We had finally decided to fish closer to shore. I agreed. We cautiously edged toward the shore, and cast out our lines. We waited and waited, but never received a bite. Just when we both had lost hope, Dad received a sharp tug. Dad fumbled with his rod for a minute, and landed a rainbow crappie.

Dad appeared content at first, but then his face went grim. "It's too small to keep," said Dad, "although it is a beautiful fish." I nodded in agreement, and set the fish back in the water. "It was a beautiful fish," I thought. The sky was beginning to get pink as the amber-orange sun began to set. Dad peered up at the sky saying, "It's about time we leave?" I nodded, and allowed Dad to pass by me to start up the engine. The engine made an awkward bubbling noise and stopped. Dad pondered the problem for a moment, and said it must be broken. I told my Dad that the only other way back would be to use the trolling motor.

Dad started up the trolling motor, and we headed off. It took a long time, but we managed to get to the dock safely. We loaded up the boat and headed off. I savored every last minute of that trip. That's why you need to check the motor twice before fishing!

# My Best Baseball Game

*John Michael Murray*
*Barfield Elementary School, Grade 3*

One day at the baseball field we were playing the number one team in coach pitch. I was up to bat with the bases loaded. I hit the ball to the fence. I ran for my life. I was rounding first base; they were running after the ball. I was rounding second, and they were at the fence. The third base coach said to go. I kept on going. The left fielder had a nice arm. He chunked it to second base. He nailed it into home. I slid into home plate before it got there. I was SAFE! I made a grand slam which means I helped the team score four runs. We won the game by one point. It was the most awesome game of my life.

# Life on a Farm

*Brennan Demarest*
*Thurman Francis Arts Academy, Grade 6*

Get up at four.
Don't be late.
Go to the yard.
Start to rake.

Plant some corn.
Squash and beans, too.
Give them some water.
And plant food.

Play the fiddle.
Hear a nice little song.
While we sing and dance.
All night long.

Life on a farm.
Is not so tough.
The only thing is.
You need to know the right stuff.


# Mrs. Levi

*Michelle Jones*
*McFadden School of Excellence, Grade 8*

You were a teacher
Not just of language
But of life
You taught right from wrong
You gave advice on everything

You were a storyteller
Your stories filled the classroom
They made us laugh till we cried
Or filled us with various emotions till we overflowed
We will never be able to forget those wonderful stories

You were an impact
You influenced all who knew you
You filled everyone you met with never-ending joy
Part of you is still stuck inside us just waiting to come out
And it does, every day

# I Remember

*Yasmeen Murtaza*
*Homer Pittard Campus School, Grade 6*


I remember dancing onstage with my friends.
And I remember the crowd cheering afterwards.

I remember decorating the tree for Christmas with beautiful bright lights and
colorful ornaments.

And I remember the sweet smells and peaceful atmosphere when I celebrated
with my family.

I remember my grandparents coming to our house to celebrate the holidays with us.
And I remember feeling calm and at home with everyone.

I remember talking with my family on my free time.
And I remember the laughs that we shared together.

I remember being at my friend's house over the summer.
And I remember the sleepovers that we had, the jokes that we made, and I remember
staying awake at night and telling secrets.

I remember my family and me going to Niagara Falls and feeling excited about seeing it
for the first time.
And I remember how amazing it looked when they shined beautiful lights on it at night.

I remember my family and me going to India and seeing my grandparents again.
And I remember the different foods we had, the great holidays that we celebrated there,
going shopping, and creating those wonderful memories.

## I Am a Special Olympic Athlete

*Grant Mayhugh*
*Smyrna Primary School, Grade 5*

I am a Special Olympic Athlete!
I love hugs!
I like bowling,
But I don't like bugs!

I have lots of friends!
I am good.
I'm very cute!
I could go to Hollywood!

I am special!
I am the best reader!
I like to read our books!
I am Grant the leader!


## The Trip to Tennessee

*Elton Ogan*
*David Youree Elementary School, Grade 3*

I used to live in Alaska. It was a long trip from Alaska to Tennessee. We rode three planes, and we rode in one car. It was boring riding on the planes, but it was fun in the car. Once we got to Tennessee, I was a lot happier. I love Tennessee!!

**Airplane** • *Katherine C. Mills* • *Lascassas Elementary School, Grade 5*

## Fun in the Sun

*Mark Johnson*
*Thurman Francis Arts Academy, Grade 6*

Last year I wrote a poem about a Wii,
This year, I am much older, as you can see.

I am bigger, stronger and taller too,
I even wear a bigger shoe.

This year I am writing about **DESTINATIONS,**
So, I will tell you about my vacation.

Florida is the state,
Location is the beach.
Beautiful ocean as far as the eye can reach.

Sunshine, waves, and suntan
Dolphins, pelicans, and crabs in the sand.

All of that may be real good,
But, I'm glad to see my neighborhood!

You go back to old friends at home,
Then your destination is back in the zone.


## My School

*Crista White*
*Smyrna Primary School, Grade 5*

I had to leave my house.
I thought I might have to leave my school.
I was really sad
Because my school is super cool!

If I could stay here it would be exciting!
If I could stay here I could learn!
If I could stay here I'd feel so safe!
If I could stay here I would have no more concern.

I like all my teachers.
I like all my friends.
I like my new bus driver.
This is the best place I've ever been.

## The Bouncy Basketball

*Matthew Wright*
*David Youree Elementary School, Grade 3*

Basketballs are hard to dribble
Over and down, in the hoop
Use your control
Never foul five times
Control and defend the ball
You will always be a winner.


## Pumpkins

*Mackenzie Wilson*
*Barfield Elementary School, Grade 2*

Pumpkins are good for carving.
Patches have pumpkins in fall.
Parents and kids are picking pumpkins.
Pumpkins are awesome!
Parents protect me at the patch.


## I Am Thankful

*Natalie Walker*
*Blackman Elementary School, Grade 2*

I am thankful for my family, friends, and teachers. Teachers are special because they help you learn. I like my friends because they are nice. I love my family because they love me. I am thankful for America because we are free.


## Childhood

*Rachel Smith*
*Barfield Elementary School, Grade 4*

Childhood is great. All the good times I love and bad times I hate. You'll have a worry every now and then. Just love and the happiness will begin. Try to sing a happy song. Ask a friend to sing along. They always cheer you up. Happiness is my favorite cup! Try to get a good friend. Friendship should never end! Love everyone that is good to you. No one should make you blue. This is why I love childhood!!

## Wall Flower

*LeAnne Hannington*
*Blackman High School, Grade 12*

We were sheltered from it all
Brick solid
Waiting for what was building up
And sneaking up
Expecting them to fall
As the rain faded all of their life pictures away

Aching inside, the envy entwined
They twisted and turned
Like eels they burned

Facing the truth
I see now the proof
A muted child on a flute
Plays us a lovely tune

Taking my knowledge
To the best of cause
Learning to love you
Was not very hard
The eyes of a stranger penetrated
But finally destroyed
I've been swept off my feet
With no more deceit
I'm able to fly


## Rattlesnake Cove

*Harrison Wrather*
*Thurman Francis Arts Academy, Grade 5*

One summer day, my brother and I went to the lake with my mom and dad, along with my grandparents, my aunt, cousin and uncle. I enjoyed spending the day swimming, riding the inner tube, riding the boat, and just having fun. We ended up parking our boats in a place called "Rattlesnake Cove." I was always told it got its name due to how it "snaked" thru the hills. After a little while of swimming, I heard several people on the opposite side of the cove screaming. So a few of us got on a wave runner to see what was going on. When we got there, a wave runner had flipped over with two people aboard and there was a very large rattle snake swimming toward them! We helped them get back on their wave runner. Luckily, no one was bitten. Now I really know how the cove got its name.

## Basketball Player

*Brinley Vinson*
*Blackman Elementary School, Grade 3*

Bound to get hurt
A lot of running
Screaming for your favorite team
Keeping the ball from the other team
Enormous fun
Talent takes all
Bouncing the ball
A lot of jerseys
Leaping up high
Loud scoreboards

Playing for fun
Laughing out loud
A lot of cheering
Yelling
Energy drinks
Rebounds


## Veteran's Day

*Zach Boisjoly*
*Blackman Middle School, Grade 6*

Dedicated to all soldiers, fallen and alive.

Veteran's Day is a day for us to give honor and pray
For those who are serving and those who have served other days
These people have gone through the cold and the grime
Sacrificing and surviving through terrible times.
So take time to recognize, honor, and pray
For Veterans from the past as well as today.


## My Memory of a Pumpkin

*Katherine Mills*
*Lascassas Elementary School, Grade 5*

Pumpkin, pumpkin, all so round
Under scarecrow on the ground
Making children jump and bound
Perfect pumpkin on the ground.
Kind face, scary face, round face, all so pleasant
In the moonlight on the ground
Nice to see you for the last time, for Halloween is over until next time.

# I Remember!

*Aubrey Perkins*
*Blackman Elementary School, Grade 4*

I remember third grade! I smell popcorn and pizza! I hear kids laughing, teachers, and computers! I see food, pencils, erasers, and sacks! I touch supplies, lunchboxes, chairs, desks, and dirt! I feel mad, sad, and happy! I remember third grade!


# First Kiss

*David Hinson*
*Smyrna High School, Grade 10*

It all started when I was at Kelsey's house about two years ago, and we were watching a movie upstairs. Through the first half of the movie all we did was hold hands. Slowly I put my arm around her, and gently she laid her head on my shoulder. Occasionally she would get scared, and she would jump and tightly grab a hold of me. Eventually she looked up at me, and I looked down at her. We stared into each other's eyes for a long minute. As we started to lean in for our first kiss, I was filled with a mix of feelings. My mind reeled, and I thought *I'm so happy, but what if I mess up?* We were now about an inch away from locking our lips together, and the only thing I was thinking was *yes! Finally we kiss,* but I didn't want to rush into the kiss. I held back and thought to myself *wait for it, wait for it...* and then all of a sudden we hear, "The pizza is here!" Oh no, it was her mom. We went downstairs to get the pizza, then back upstairs to start our second movie.

We were watching The Descent. It was another scary movie, and I thought it would set the mood again. I put my arm around her quicker now, and five minutes into the movie we were staring into each others eyes again. I was praying that nothing else would go wrong. We looked at each other again, and we began moving toward each other, and this time all we heard was . . . the great sound of silence! Yes, that's right, we finally kissed that night.


# Halloween Night

*Bailee Sherrill*
*Walter Hill Elementary School, Grade 2*

On Halloween night we go to a friend's house. The pumpkins are shinning and the fire is hot! Everyone is dressed up that night. Our tummies are full with hot dogs and marshmallows when it is time to go. The tractor is starting. Beep! Beep! The horn blows. It must be time to trick or treat. With a sack full of candy my night was a real treat!

## I Remember!

*Matthew Jobe*
*Blackman Elementary School, Grade 4*

I remember Halloween! I smell candy and trees! I hear boo and trick-or-treat! I see lots of people, candy bags, and skeletons! I touch candy, doors, and my Halloween costume! I feel scared, excited, and nervous! I remember Halloween!

## The King

*Josie Wornstaff*
*Walter Hill Elementary School, Grade 2*

I dreamed that I met Elvis Presley at a motel. He had the fanciest room ever! He had a huge flat screen television and a disco ball that lit up the room! He shaked, rattled and rolled all night. And that, my friends, is why they call him "THE KING!" Thank you; thank you very much.

## Maryland

*Christine Monchecourt*
*Blackman Elementary School, Grade 5*

My best friends live there
And they were lots of fun.
Riding to the ice cream shop,
Yummy bubble gum.
Lollygagging all day long,
And singing a silly song.
Now I live so far away,
Don't forget me, let me stay.

# My Very Own Expectations

*Gabby Chesak*
*Stewarts Creek Elementary School, Grade 5*

I am a talented fifth grade student that is athletic, smart, and funny. I am great at some things, but on the other hand I could do better at other things, too.

I think I do well in soccer. While I play the position forward, the wind runs into my face and hair like it is whispering in my ear telling me what I should do. As I gingerly sprint with the ball, I think of all I learned from my awesome Coach Paul. I set up goals and sometimes make goals. At the end of every game we win, my team and I jump with jubilation while chanting our team cheer.

I think I could do better at skateboarding. I need to face my fears and do more ollies and go down more ramps. I am brave and tough as nails on the soccer field, but nervousness takes over me at the skate park because I am afraid I could be seriously injured. I sometimes think about how brave and courageous skateboarders are at the BMX games. Maybe I should be braver, too.

**Destination to Anywhere** • *Chris Gregory* • *Siegel High School, Grade 12*

# Kaleigh Smotherman

*Kaleigh Smotherman*
*David Youree Elementary School, Grade 3*

I am me.
I am a good friend.
I am an American.
I am nice.
I think I am funny.
I am scared of snakes.
I feel happy.
I am happy when I am with my family.
I was sad when I lost my dog.
I want to go to Hawaii.
I want to be an animal doctor.
I want to play softball.
I am a good friend.
I am an American.
I am nice.
I am me.


# A Fun Trip to the Pumpkin Patch!

*Payton Hershel*
*Blackman Elementary School, Grade 3*

In kindergarten, I went to the pumpkin patch. My mom brought my lunchbox because we were having a picnic on a hill.

After the picnic, we walked around the pumpkin patch. Then we tried out some activities out, like the balancing log. It was kind of wobbling, but it was still joyous. The class, my mom, and I went to a barn. There was a playhouse too! The class and I were enjoying it. We also picked out some pumpkins and put them in bags.

Then we got back on the bus and drove back to school. On the way there, I fell asleep. When we got there, my mom woke me up. Then we went back home. It was my most exciting trip of my life.

# A Far Away Place

*Tristan Jones-Tauti*
*Stewarts Creek Middle School, Grade 7*

I wish there was a land,
Or a far away place,
Where I could be alone,
With my cat Mace,
Where there wouldn't be bullies,
Shoving food in my face,
It would be me, and me alone,
Oh, how I dream of this far away place.

I dream of this place,
This far away land,
Where my siblings, the bullies,
Won't put sand down my pants,
Or take me to the zoo,
Then push me into the elephants,
I would be by myself,
My cat Mace and I
Oh how I dream of this far away place.

I think of this land, of this far away dream,
Where some things aren't always
Just as they seem,
This hope, though,
This dream,
Is just that, a dream,
And here, things are always
Just as they seem.
Here in the U.S.,
The land of the free.

# Tokyo

*Grant Chindavong*
*Blackman Elementary School, Grade 5*

The land of the rising sun
Of the beautiful pink and white cherry blossoms
Kyushu and other great lands
Yamato the great Shogun in old Japanese times
Onigiri, a traditional rice ball wrapped in seaweed

# My First Day of School in America

*Ismael Rodriguez*
*Smyrna High School, Grade 12*

My alarm rang at 6:30 A.M.

"Wake up!" my uncle yelled at me.

I got up and took a shower. After I got out of the bathroom, my uncle was already waiting for me outside. We drove in silence to school. On the way I was thinking about my old school in Mexico. Would it be anything like that at Smyrna?

As we arrived at Smyrna High School, I was so nervous because I was not sure what I was supposed to do. I did not say a word as we walked into school and went straight to the office. They asked my uncle a lot of information about me. Not knowing English, I did not understand what they were talking about. After a while, they took me to my first class. I met my teacher and she put me in the last chair in the classroom. At 8:30, the classroom began to get full of students. Everyone was looking at me without saying a word.

"Good morning, everybody," my new teacher said. "I want to get to know everybody, so when I call your name, tell me something about your summer vacation."

I was so scared because I did not speak a word of English, and I did not understand what she was saying.

"Okay, let me start with you in the first row."

"My name is Raquel," a very pretty girl began. She talked a little bit about what she did in the summer, but I did not understand anything besides her name.

"Next," the teacher said. The next person in the row began.

I was so scared. I looked down at the desk thinking two more people and then she will call my name. Finally it was my turn. I stood up and my face turned red. My legs were shaking and I felt so bad that I thought I was about to cry. If it could have been possible, I began to feel worse because it was right then that I noticed everyone's eye upon me. I could not say anything. Words did not come out of my mouth. After a while the teacher came up to me.

"Ismael, do you speak any English at all? If you do not, tell me but do not worry about it. It is okay. You will learn it. The reason why I am working here is to help students learn English."

Ring, ring, ring. The bell rang to dismiss class. Everybody got up and left class, but I did not know what to do. My teacher walked me to my next class. I think that day was the worst day of my life. I still remember it like it was yesterday, but now I sit in class, and I am able to write this story in English.

# The Good Days

*Mickey Wells*
*Smyrna High School, Grade 10*

Most people don't understand that small incidents from our past define us and make up who we are today.

The day started out like any other. My mom dropped me off at the Freeman's house to spend one of the many summer days playing and fighting with the four Freeman brothers. They were all around my age so the arrangement worked quite well. On this particular day, however, we were preparing for war.

We had decided to attack our now-mortal-enemy, the hornets. The hornets had invaded our tree house over the spring, and we couldn't play in or around our favorite hangout. We plotted the hornitos' demise in the garage, as well as acquired our weapons.

I donned my armor composed of shoulder pads, a catcher's breast plate, football helmet, shin guards, hockey gloves, elbow pads, and my weapon of choice was a hockey stick.

My mission was to go into the tree house and knock the hornet's nest to the ground, while everyone else sprayed it with a hose and super-soakers, or so the plan went.

After I successfully got up to the tree house without incident, I thought it would be a breeze. I leaned out the window so I could see the nest. I guided the hockey stick next to the huge structure. Just as I was about to knock the catacomb down, what seemed like a thousand hornets burst from the hive causing me to lose my balance and fall out of the window to the hard earth below. As soon as I hit the ground, I knew there was something seriously wrong. I looked over to see my arm was broken.

The Freeman brothers still tease me to this day about that trip to the emergency room when I was pleading for the doctor not to cut off my arm. When I look back at it, I can't help but laugh. Some people don't understand that something that seems so insignificant defines a person's character and molds them into who they are now.


# My Favorite Dream Ever

*Tyesha Anthony*
*Kittrell Elementary School, Grade 3*

I went to a place called Go Singers. I had a great time. I got to meet other singers named Joe Jonas, Nick Jonas, and Jason Jones. We got gifts. All of us had a lot of things in common, like singing and dancing. We rehearsed and rehearsed so we could sing together. Then we sang together and everyone loved it. People took a lot of pictures of us. Then we became friends and famous.

## Christmas Night

*Kevin Darrell*
*Buchanan Elementary School, Grade 5*

Tonight is Christmas night
Boy, the sky is bright.
Hoping Santa will come
Stuffing stockings with a plum.
Making cookies and milk
Wrapping myself in smooth silk.
I heard a thump on the wall
Boy, it surprised us all.
Go to see what is up
Then I heard another thump.
Thump, thump, thump!
Bump, bump, bump!
Santa!

**Christmastime** • *Rex Hutchins* • *Barfield Elementary School, Grade 2*

# Fall

*Sunshine Scott*
*Rockvale Middle School, Grade 6*

Fall is my favorite of all seasons
Now I will tell you the reasons
Fall is loads of fun
When you get outside and run
It's not quite hot
And not quite cold
That's why fall never gets old
There are leaves of different colors
Like orange and red
I love when the leaves
That fall on my head
Fall is one of my favorite seasons
I'm glad I told you the reasons

# A Thanksgiving Memory

*Sarah Simmons*
*Eagleville School, Grade 12*

It's Thanksgiving Day, it's crisp and cool.
Mom's laboring away preparing the feast.
Children are running around making plenty of noise;
Just the thought of the upcoming food is enough to make one drool.

It is a disaster as people rush to make their plates.
Food is piled on, as if a famine just ended.
Pushing and shoving begins as family fights for their favorite dishes.
But when everyone begins to sit, the always tardy aunt arrives late.

We all look for a seat and find our right places.
A little crowded, yes we are, but that's the last thing on our minds.
Our plates are full of delicious foods we have waited a year for.
Before we dig in, someone is designated to say grace.

Plates are raked clean by everyone there.
But seconds are a given, foods are piled up once again.
Then dessert is retrieved with impatient haste.
After we all finish it's time to relax, so we find a comfy chair.

The women sit and chat, while at the football game the men cheer.
We reflect on the day and all agree, we can't wait until next year!

# From Cancer to College

*Jacob Boone*
*Oakland High School, Grade 12*

I often asked the question, why I am so short. Sometimes I'll just laugh and say that is how God made me, but usually I give them the whole story. My story is this; at eighteen months old I was diagnosed with cancer, more specifically neuroblastoma, which basically means that I had a tumor on my left kidney. After two years of chemotherapy, radiation, and a bone marrow transplant I was pronounced in remission in the spring of 1993. Since then I have been a pretty healthy child with some side effects; for example stunted growth, cataracts in both eyes, and allergies. Through the years I have endured these side affects with some grief, though as I grew older and wiser I realized that my Lord God has a plan for me on this earth, and there is a reason why I have undergone all these trials. So as I reach the end of my senior year, I will start my next destination in college where I seek God's plan for me.


# My Favorite Gift

*Tyler Hoggard*
*Rockvale Middle School, Grade 6*

I came home on Christmas Eve. It had been a wonderful day. I walked to the doorsteps and saw cloud-like figures dancing in the air. It was snowing! I walked in the house with a glorious feeling. It was a feeling that you could only get on Christmas Eve. My mom saw me walk in and said, "You are probably very cold, come lie down." But I am not sleepy" I argued wearily. "You get some sleep before it's too late" Mom said. I bit back a sharp retort and let myself rest.

I was in a vision. It was a vision of a beautiful place, like such only in dreams. It was snowy and clear at the same time, yet bright and dark too. I saw my mom, dad, and sister. They saw me and said, "This is a Christmas of dreams. You will awake and find yourself home, in your room, knowing what your favorite present will be." After that, they left me in my world of dreams.

I woke and was on my bed sitting up, waiting for my family to call me. "Ready to open presents?" It was my dad. I quickly jumped out of my bed and ran into the living room. It was full of gifts, blue, yellow, and bright red. It was like in my dream, so beautiful. I suddenly realized what my favorite present was. It was the present. Yesterday was the past, tomorrow is the future, and today is a gift. That's why we call it the "present."

## The Destiny Stealer

*Caleb Miles*
*Oakland High School, Grade 12*

I once had the ability to fly. Ascending from the ground as I approached my destiny, I had no question of how or why. I knew that this was supposed to happen, that it was the path for me. I could see in the distance an enormous figure, an enigma to the naked eye. I was unable to make out its shape as half of its body was in the clouds. It began to weave in and out of the cloudy mist like a lioness through the tall grass as she approaches her prey. As it drew nearer, I found that it was no longer an enigma; it was a dragon. The grotesque beast was closing in so fast; I had no time to gracefully descend by the way I came. So I just fell towards the ground like a bolt of lightning cast down by God himself.

I gazed up at the gloomy sky only to see the dragon pursuing me still. Every fiber of my being was terrified, until I began to see a change in the dragon's form as it approached. The monstrous figure began to shrink as it glided towards me. It wasn't until it flew right into the palm of my hand that I discovered it was just a wooden toy. I gazed down feeling fooled by my own fears and dismayed for I no longer had the ability to fly. A life's lesson was learned that day; never let your fears prevent you from spreading your wings, because in the end, you will discover your dragon is nothing but a mere wooden toy.

## The Bike Race

*Owen Krugh*
*Lascassas Elementary School, Grade 1*

When I was little I rode my bike in the nashinal bike race 5 miles and I came in 1st place. I came in 1st place 10 times. Do you like to run and ride to? I hope so.

## Trustworthiness

*Lorenzo Smith*
*Smyrna Primary School, Grade 1*

Trustworthiness means I tel the trooth. It makes me feel prowd!
It helps me help uther pepl. It can make uther pepl hapy! It helps me stay on track!

# Marshmallows

*Haley Smith*
*Thurman Francis Arts Academy, Grade 5*

"Yawn!" I blinked my eyes before my window because the bright morning sun was beaming through the curtains. It was a fresh Monday morning, even though school was the last thing I wanted to do. I forced myself to stretch and looked over at the clock. "SNAP!" I yelled as I discovered the time was two minutes until seven'o clock which is when we are *supposed* to be leaving for school! I popped out of bed and ran into my mom's room yelling at her to wake up! She lifted her head up, put it back down, and told me to go look outside. As I crept to the window slowly and confused, I peeked out only to discover to my surprise, there was a thick layer of fluffy, pure white snow resting softly on the ground. I bolted back to my room and threw on a sweatshirt, a coat, gloves a scarf, and my favorite pink polka dotted snow boots. I ran back into my mom's room and she started laughing because she said I looked like a marshmallow! LAME! I ignored her joke and strode out the back door. The snow was very bright and deeper than I imagined, maybe up to my shins. I spent that day building snowmen, making snow angels, snow castles, and snow forts. I had a blast that surprise snowy day! My mom made me come inside every little while to thaw out by the fire and have some hot chocolate with extra marshmallows of all things. After a fun day, I was tired and it was time for bed. I awakened the next morning only to find that the snow was gone and I was headed to school. But, I had a feeling it would be back next year; I just knew it would!


# Why Do I Cry?

*Conrad W. Mercado-Torres*
*Roy Waldron School, Grade 5*

Why oh why
Do I cry?
I whine and whine
While my mother says,
"It's just fine."
I cried all night. My mother
Kissed me and sighed,
And tucked me in tight.
After that night, I
Was all right.

# Where Our Time Will Go

*Courteney Rodriguez*
*Blackman Middle School, Grade 8*

> I make my way slowly
> Though there isn't much time
> But what is time but a number
> Snaking its way by
> Sliding through our fingers
> Like so many grains of sand
> Until there is nothing
> Left in our hands?
> So let's grasp those grains
> And hold time to our hearts
> For when we're together,
> No longer apart
> We'll both show our palms
> And let all ounces of our eternity fly
> To be caressed by the wind
> To be blown into the sky
> Into the weather worn gloves
> Of some tired, foreign traveler
> Who happens to have none left.

# Roc the Great Eagle

*Duncan Sandefur*
*Stewarts Creek Elementary School, Grade 5*

Clomp!....Clomp!....Clomp!...was the sound of my boots stomping like an angry bull as I went on a hike through the woods. Then, I heard a huge silence-piercing **SHRRRRIIIEEEEK!!** that was too big to fit on one line of this page. So, I shortened it.

It made a huge streak of light shine on me as if the trees were scared, too. Then, I ran towards where the shriek came from. Next, I spotted millions of what seemed like tiny, little footprints; they came from a tormented bush.

So, I followed the tracks that led to something humongous, feathery, brown, white, and yellow. I stepped back, and I saw the BIGGEST Bald Eagle ever!

But it was trapped in a net. "Poachers!" I thought. I took out my pocket knife and cut the ropes. It must have been magical because it said, "Thank you, a poacher did that to me, but I took care of him. I shall grant you one wish; what shall it be?" I said, "One of your golden feathers." He gave one to me and I darted home. The feather was magical, too. So now I can sprout wings and fly as high as an eagle as long as I have the feather with me.

135

# Where I'm Going

*Keaton Shearron*
*Oakland High School, Grade 12*

I'm leaving childhood
And running straight into...
Adulthood?
I'm not sure I'm ready.

Are my bags packed?
Did I remember to bring
Compassion?
Honesty?
Courage?
Wisdom?

And what did I leave behind?
Did I learn enough?
Did I laugh enough?
Did I love enough?
Did I live enough?

I must leave.
I must move forward into
The life planned out for me.
Okay, maybe I am ready.

The path ahead is unclear,
but I know each step will be lighted by
Your patience
Your example
Your unfailing love
Your hand in mine.

Here I go...

## Letter to Veterans
*Sydney Bullock*
*Smyrna Primary School, Grade 1*

Dear Veterans,
        I'm glad you keep us safe.  I am glad you work for the world.
I am so glad you keep the world safe.

                                                I love you,
                                                Sydney


## Shuck in Shack Corn Maze
*Madilyn Grisham*
*Lascassas Elementary School, Grade 1*

I went to Shuck in Shack Corn Maze and I picked a pumckin and my sister did to.  We went through the big maze.  It was fun.


## Your Destination
*Masataku Okamura*
*Siegel Middle School, Grade 8*

You had tears you hid from everybody
You came a long way trying to find your light
It wasn't a plain, easy path.
You got over the wall, which was yourself, so many times
The steps you took were sometimes painful
But beyond yourself and painfulness,
There is the light just for you
Now it is time
To step into your destination.


## Tae Kwon Do Rocks!
*Camden Temple*
*Cedar Grove Elementary School, Grade 1*

US Tae Kwon Do is very important to me.  It makes me strong and powerful.  The better I get the higher rank I am. I have an orange belt with a blue stripe on it.  I will work hard to be a black belt.  My family loves to watch me practice my form and high kicks.  I am really good.

# Change

*Ashley Sarten*
*Blackman Middle School, Grade 8*

I hit.
I hate.
I don't wish to be this way.
I fear I may start drugs.
I fear I may kill.
Then I remember.
I have friends.
They help me through it all.
Then I realize,
I may be able to reach it.

Who do I want to be?
A better person
A better friend
Now I love.
I hug.
I care,
And I thank only my
Friends!

# Cherch

*Maclay Bowers*
*Lascassas Elementary School, Grade 1*

Every Sunday me and my grand perents go to church. We sit in rows of chers. We go
to the library every time. We go back to the rows of chers then we go home and we eat
lunch. Then I go to my house and I ride my horse.

# When I Am Big

*Jacob Wilson*
*Smyrna Primary School, Grade 2*

To write books is fun.
I'd like to be an author.
It's interesting!

## Stand Up

*Annabelle Tran*
*Blackman Middle School, Grade 8*

Reach up from behind the shadows.
Make your voice be heard.
Stand tall, stand proud
No more hiding behind the way.
The wall separates you from it all.
Make history behind your name.
Stand up for what is right, not wrong.
Don't put anything to shame.
Stand up and make a statement.
Reach others where no one has reached.
Touch their souls with your passion.
Make things last forever.
Life is too short to hate and not love,
So stand up and make a statement.


## Life in the Streets

*Silvestre Juarez*
*Daniel McKee Alternative School, Grade 11*

Life in the streets.
Everyone gets up to go and meet.
All have love for the streets.
Many people make money.
Some just go and greet.
Few get hurt, and a couple of homeboys
    go to jail.
Many pray that they live another day.
Somewhere is the smell of a cook-out.
The sound of music is filling the air.
Someone's laughter and love is in the air.
All in another day of —
Life in the streets.

# Let Me Decide

*Tiffany Young*
*Siegel Middle School, Grade 8*

Give my little wishes,
My own clothes,
My own honor,
A chance to make my own mistakes.
To grow my own special gardens,
Tolerate my musings,
As I learn
And change my mind.
Don't lead me or I won't learn to walk alone,
To see or speak my heart.
Listen before you judge me,
For I feel deeply and have reason to.
Remember I must discover
Different dreams before I can find
What my interest approves.
Trust my actions and my choices
However different from your own.
Give me the stability to take chances,
To know that if I fail,
I'm not alone.
Let me know that where I'm coming from
Is a safe place to return.
Allow me the boldness to be creative.
The chance to be myself.
Teach me that I don't have to be
Perfect or strong to belong.
Give me my own secrets, my own music,
My own space to grow.
Learn with me as I discover my one, new destination.
My true eternity,
My final destiny,
My forever legacy.
In this ever-changing world.
Where everyone has
Those two destinations.
Please....
Just let me decide.

## Without Anxiety
*Taylor Fitzpatrick*
*Blackman Middle School, Grade 8*

Without anxiety. . .
Wouldn't that be nice?
A world to reside in without paying the price,
A place where there are no fights,
A time to share the joys in life, instead of watching all of the strife,
A world where life is in your hands, to hold and to treasure and to make plans,
Worries gone for time to come so you can sit back and see what your life has become,
A place to relax and never stress,
A place where everything isn't a mess,
A place where dreams really do come true,
A time to show the plans you drew,
The one destination where a plan will not fall through,
A place to enjoy life as it comes and goes,
A journey to embark on without any foes
A world without anxiety.
Wouldn't that be nice?


## Computer Repair Shop
*Cory Sain*
*Daniel McKee Alternative School, Grade 11*

Computer Repair

Everyone's computer is broken.
Something smells inside it.
Somewhere is a broken part.
Anyone see it?
No one knows what to do.
Some of the computers are shot.
None of the parts are in stock.
Somebody order some more!

Computer Repair

## Hayden

*Hayden White*
*Blackman Elementary School, Grade 1*

**H**appy is this little boy
**A**lways playing with toys
**Y**esterday he was small
**D**aily he is getting tall
**E**verybody loves him very much
**N**aughty hardly ever; mom says thanks a bunch


## Alone

*Barry Huff*
*Smyrna West Alternative School, Grade 8*

I feel like an outsider being treated differently,
I feel a hammer of sorrow is banging my head,
I feel like no one understands who I am or who I wanna be,
I feel I'm in a world that doesn't understand me,
I feel alone.


## Madness

*Benjamin Hunt*
*Smyrna High School, Grade 12*

Geometric madness all around
Live and work by the clock
Down the crowded halls
Popularity is everything
Immured by conformity
Genius loses
to fake intelligence
Nice guy gives girl everything
Girl picks status king
The dreamer and mystic
Was never lonelier
Find escape in the dream world
Follow the crowd or be cast out
Be in the middle of the crowd or the middle of your mind.

# Life of a Gymnast

*MaryGrace Bouldin*
*Homer Pittard Campus School, Grade 4*


Football is almost as hard as gymnastics.
Beam is like walking on the top of a fence.
Vault is like running full speed towards a brick wall.
Bars are like swinging on gas pipes.
Floor may have lots of dancing;
But tumbling is like flipping on concrete.
Blisters hurt as bad as a bee sting.
But the victory feels like you own the world.


# Tomorrow

*Ryan Bruley*
*Lascassas Elementary School, Grade 4*


Every day when I get home from school, I wonder what will happen tomorrow. Will I miss school for some reason; will I go on a vacation? Minutes and hours pass by, and still I wonder what will happen.

One day while I was asleep, I dreamed my class and I were doing exciting activities and going outside. I dreamed that I had no homework. I woke up and got ready for school. While I was at school, I realized that some of the things in my dream were coming true! We got to go outside, and I had no homework that night!

When I got home, I wondered once again, *What will happen tomorrow?*

# Coach Malone

*Scott Humphrey*
*Smyrna West Alternative School, Grade 10*

I remember the hot summer days we spent practicing,
And the disappointing look on your face when we did something wrong.

I remember the way you yelled to make us work harder,
And the smiles when we did well.

I remember our dirty pants after a hard-won game.

I remember the late night practices getting ready for the game,
And I remember the smile on your face when I struck the batters out.

And if I struggled, you calmed me down and helped me out.

I remember your one-on-one's to help me become a star pitcher.

I remember the way you looked so sad when I had to leave the team 'cuz I was told I was too old.

And I will always remember the tips you gave me to help me through life.

But Coach Malone, I will remember you most for the man you helped me become.


# Misunderstood

*Devin Henderson*
*Smyrna West Alternative School, Grade 9*

In my life I'm misunderstood
In my life I think I should
But I'm just misunderstood

They say I do this
They say I do that
But they don't know
I'm not like that

I get questioned
I get accused
They say that's what I do

In my life
I say I should
I think I could
But sadly I'm just misunderstood

# I'm from What Makes Me, Me

*Kelsey Robertson*
*Siegel High School, Grade 11*

I'm from me,
Where sugar and spice combine to make an explosion.

I'm from a familiar black roof hovering over red bricks on a subdivision street,
With a violet door that's always welcoming.

I'm from a little girl with her chestnut hair in pigtails playing with her dolls,
Who magically morphed into a grown young lady with colossal aspirations and hopes.

I'm from steaming, delectable gravy and biscuits in the early morning,
Concocted from the wonder-working hands of my petite, loving Granny Jo.

I'm from the care of two loving parents,
Who have always taught me that the sky's not the limit, but to zoom to the stars.

I'm from the little white country church nestled between two rolling hills,
Where it's the temporary home to a sprinkle of sinners just passing through this world.

I'm from losing antic battles with my frivolous older brother,
And sniggering heartily when he got penalized by my angry parents.

I'm from doing mediocre jumps and flips around my house,
With the hope of cheering up a rowdy crowd one day.

I'm from picking potatoes and shucking corn on a diminutive country farm,
And enjoying the Lynchburg sun playing hide-and-seek behind the horizon line.

I'm from the comfortable protective wings of my eldest brother,
Who never took his fatherly eyes off me.

I'm from sitting in a run-down lawn chair in the front yard with my granddaddy,
And clinging desperately to his every word of wisdom before he went home to be with God.

I'm from a dream of one day living in the glamorous California,
Where I daydream about the deep blue ocean that greets the light blue sky.

I'm from wanting one thing more than anything else in this astronomical world,
And hopefully someday I can call myself a respectable writer.

I'm from the fear of what will happen tomorrow,
And then immediately having contentment rush through me as God whispers, "It's okay."

I'm from a sturdy past
That makes a dependable, fruitful future.

I'm from me.

## Tired Already

*Kelly Sypraseut*
*Smyrna High School, Grade 11*

When you wake up you're tired already,
But once you get up, your pace will be steady.
For you must do your job and work on it hard,
'Cause the world takes no breaks, it's just you that would stop.
The world is not kind, it won't wait a minute.
For once you are late, your work goes unfinished.
You sometimes take breaks if your boss says you can,
For he understands you're just a hard working man.
You finish your work but no one says "Thank You,"
But don't get mad, they could just replace you.
So just go back home and shut off your phone
And go back to bed and get your self ready,
For tomorrow again you'll wake up tired already.

## All Alone

*Alex Echeverria*
*Smyrna West Alternative School, Grade 9*

My brothers are the only ones that care
When Dad says I'm the reason for his divorce.
My brothers are the only ones that protect me
When Dad gets mad and cocks his fists.
My brothers are the only ones that say, "Don't listen."
When my friends say I ain't nothin'
My brothers are the only ones who love me
When I'm all alone in this cold, dark world.

# As the Rain Falls

*Taylor Humphrey*
*Smyrna High School, Grade 11*

My true awakening came with the first raindrop.
Cool to the skin
Flushing and relaxing
I was coated with the spirit of rebirth.
My mind was able to open.
All struggle
All stress
Washed away,
Allowing rest and relaxation,
Freedom,
And open reception for wisdom.
As the rain mixed with my tears,
All my fears sought resort by dripping from my chin.
That release opened a portal,
A portal of mental and spiritual recovery.
New emotions were waiting for discovery.
Each prism of truth and serenity,
Crystallized in my mind
Leaving its flowing form behind.
Each small piece
Brought together a picture perfect puzzle,
Allowing my eyes to see clearly.

Truth,
Knowledge,
Understanding,
And wisdom were falling on me.
Every part of me
Absorbing it exclusively.
Every negative aspect I held near and dear,
Dissolved like salt in water,
Only leaving room for the positive.
Thoughts I never knew I could think,
Emotions I never knew I could feel,
Perspectives I never dreamed I could see,
All became so real.
Tangible yet idealistic,
My new state of mind.
Growing rapidly,
With no intention of stopping,
Until the clouds ran dry.
Through blur of heavy rain,
Everything was clearly defined.

Every object had shape.
Every detail was fine.
The rain was flowing through my body,
Effectively cleansing my soul.
My purpose in life,
Now whole.
My new mind,
Waiting to unfold.
With the cure of the rain,
now told.
Rain,
Nature's personal cleansing system,
Lets Earth rebirth
And opens my mind to its inner spirituality.
The new outlook formed with each raindrop that touched my skin.
Now,
Now,
My new life begins.


## Where I'm From

*Samantha Erickson*
*Eagleville School, Grade 12*

I am from sunny afternoons,
Playing in my old backyard as a kid.
From funny stories told around the supper table
And family gatherings on the Fourth of July.

I am from slumber parties and late night girl talks
Games of truth or dare with movies and popcorn.
From times of joy and sadness,
Love and heartbreak.

I am from RC Cola and moon pies at my grandmother's
Freeze pops and milkshakes at my aunt's.
From chicken noodle soup when I caught a cold
And stories told before bedtime.

## Cut Away

*Blake Garrett*
*McFadden School of Excellence, Grade 8*

I will never forget that fatal day.
The day it all got cut away.
You'll never believe how it went down.
The event that left me with a great big frown.
My mom said, "You need a haircut now."
So Logan said, "Sit down, Blake. I'll show you how."
I trusted him, which was my biggest mistake.
For I didn't know he was the biggest fake.
So Logan started to cut away
But no one knew just what to say.
It had looked like a lawnmower had come my way
But Logan laughed and went on with his day
The memory of my hair is always in my heart
Because that day I wasn't very smart.


## Confused

*Matt Sellars*
*Smyrna West Alternative School, Grade 9*

Everything I do leaves me confused.
I can never find my way.
It's like being lost in a giant cave.
Looking left and right
up and down
Just to start all over again.
It's so confusing, I was so close
But nothing ever changes.
Only time goes by.
Feeling lost in my mind.
It hurts to be so confused.
I do not wish to ever share
this life of pain
no one could bear.

## Big Bass, Little Bass

*Jacob Jewell*
*Eagleville School, Grade 12*

Big bass, little bass,
Everyone's the same,
No matter the size,
The fight is the gain.
Big bass, little bass,
Your heart will always skip a beat,
The second the bass bites,
Your mind goes blank.
Thankful for the trophy
On the other end.
Big bass, little bass
They're always the same…in the end.


## All About Me

*Kayla Brewer*
*David Youree Elementary School, Grade 3*

I am me.
I am honest.
I am pretty.
I am a friend.
I am thankful for my sister.
I am scared of the dark.
I feel giddy.
I am happy when my dogs play with me.
I am sad when I have to leave home.
I want to go to the beach.
I want to be a teacher.
I want to stay with my mom.
I am honest.
I am a friend.
I am me.

# It's Sad When

*Sarai Price*
*Riverdale High School, Grade 11*

It's sad when…
People we know
Become people we knew
When people we always go to
Become people we always avoid
When people we love
Become typical strangers
When great friends
Become great acquaintances
When secret keepers
Become secret tellers
When silent promises
Become non-existent promises
When a helpful word of advice
Becomes a twisted weapon against the giver
When something small and harmless
Becomes enormously blown out of proportion
When what was once united
Becomes shattered
When one was once whole
Becomes terribly broken
When what was
Becomes too painful to remember
When one tries to fix what they purposely broke
Becomes too mangled to fix
When we used to seek each other out
But now we can no longer look each other in the eyes
My dear old friend
Don't you see what's become of us?
We're the typical lie.

# A Treasure of Thoughts

*Courtney Goodman*
*McFadden School of Excellence, Grade 7*

So here I am
Just plain me
There's nothing special
There's nothing to see

But there's something more
Something completely new
A thing you can't see
From your point of view

Just dig deep inside
And you might find
My greatest treasure
That is my mind

My thoughts and secrets
Will never escape
Hopes and dreams
Will stay hidden away

So only the ones
Who really try
Will get to see
Inside my mind

So go ahead
Try to figure me out
If you take the chance
You'll find what I'm truly about

# Progression

*Victoria Richardson*
*Siegel High School, Grade 11*

I have seen people laugh
I have seen them all cry
I have seen them exuberant
While some wished to die
A lonely dark corner
That's where I hid
Away from the world
Disconnected
That was my home
Where I once stayed
But now no longer
A new home was made
For in the darkness
A light had been seen
Tucked in the darkness
That's where I have been

It began as a glimmer
Dull, dark, and morose
A stagnant dim shimmer
But something arose
I stood from my corner
My head tilted high
And with a suddenness
A truth caught my eye
Rejuvenation, renewal
Rebirth and repent
These gifts the Lord
My God had now sent
And with these blessings
A road was conceived
Filled with such things
I would never have believed
But I swallow my doubt
And clutch His sound hand
I march steadily onward
To where I now stand

Through a steady belief
In the King in the sky
I wish for the happiness
That I was denied
The ability to smile

To laugh and to love
Without fearing rebuke
A push or a shove
But all this requires
Time and patience
For I am not there
In need of guidance
But just when this will be
There's no way of knowing
Only that I understand
This is where I am going.


# Where I'm From

*Sanna Ali*
*Siegel High School, Grade 10*

I am from sandstorms of Kuwait
And calm winds of Tennessee,
From bread crumbs of ducks behind the trees

I am from the love of my mom – a chef no less than Rachel Ray
And my dad – who seems to love me more and more every day
Also from my friends who taught me to take a chance

I am from the grains of "biryani" to Taco Bell drive thrus
From lime green walls that surround me
And the melting in my mouth of milk Cadbury

I am from a rumbling, multicolor ball
All the way to the dent on my head, that happened because of a wall
From that once dream house like Toys R US

I am from the Big Ben in London
And Disney World in Florida
From a camel ride in southern Asia

I am from a pink Barbie convertible
From the purple dinosaur that wouldn't bite
And a red Power Ranger costume on Halloween night
I am from the white winter snow
And from beautiful beach sunsets
From the soft, light rains that fall every so often

I am from my first word "Mama," which I still hold to my lips.

## Big and Beautiful

*Charlita Hunt*
*Smyrna West Alternative School, Grade 10*

Just because I'm big
  Doesn't mean I eat a lot
  Or I don't have any friends
Just because I'm big
  I'm not lazy
  I'm not shy
Just because I'm big
  Doesn't mean I feel any less about myself
Just because I'm big
  I'm not emotional
  I'm not hated
Just because I'm big
  Doesn't mean I have low self-esteem
Just because I'm big
  I'm not fake
  I can dress to impress
Just because I'm big
  Doesn't mean I can't get a date
Just because I'm big
  People wanna judge me
Just because I'm big
  I'm not nasty
  I'm not sloppy
Just because I'm big—let me realize my beauty.


## Skating is Fun!

*Chandler Corlew*
*Smyrna Primary School, Grade 2*

My family lets me go skating. My brother just learned how to skate. I bring a lot of friends to skate with me. When we go skating, I get the speed kind. Next, I play the games. Skating is fun!

# Elements of a Beautiful History

*Sarena Rhody*
*Siegel High School, Grade 11*

I am from a little town in the heart of the Tennessee countryside
Where secrets are few and breathtaking sunrises and sunsets are plenty
Where churches are small and close knit; where everybody knows who got saved last
Sunday
Where schools are so old that your grandparents went there, too
And Starbucks is practically a myth
And German cars are few
Where Wal-Mart is more of a favorite local hangout than a grocery store

I am from Twix bars and Momma's back rubs when I just can't get to sleep
From Daddy's pancakes on snowy mornings
And endless pints of melting Ben and Jerry's ice cream dripping from a cone on
summer days
From church every single Sunday and Wednesday

I'm from a family of music, music, music!
It rings from my heart, as clear as a bell.
From long, sweltering August band practices to teeth-chattering November editions
Concert band brings even more beautiful songs for me to hum throughout the day
Jackson Browne lulling me into a peaceful sleep night after night

I'm from long Sunday afternoons stretching out endlessly with long comfy catnaps
filling in the gaps.
Weekday afternoon lake runs
Because weekends are simply too busy for our boards to get the glass they desire

I'm from a certain smiling, brown-haired boy promising me that everything will be ok
day after stressful day.
From songs sung over the phone to hugs every morning
With all the happiness I'll ever need

I am from a life of unpredictability
But a still consistently warm and happy life
A life of laughter and joy
I'm the product of a merciful Savior's grace
And a wonderful place I call home

## The Doctor

*Hannah Moran*
*Barfield Elementary School, Grade 2*

A doctor is a special person that helps people who are sick or hurt. A doctor helped me when I broke my arm. I liked the doctor's office. It was fun. Now my arm is healed. I am very happy that my arm is better. Now I can play.

## I Shine

*Addie Raymer*
*Barfield Elementary School, Grade 2*

I climb,
I rhyme,
It's fun to shine your light
Every day and every night.
You will smile at yourself
For working so hard,
For traveling so far.
I climb,
I rhyme,
I shine

## Guilt

*Campbell Hunt*
*Blackman Middle School, Grade 6*

Guilt is a feeling
It is always biting at your heels
Getting you to remember your biggest mistakes and troubles
It's the feeling you get when you forget a promise that you made to a friend.
It's the feeling you get if you hit an animal while driving on the road.
Guilt is the feeling that reminds you that you can't undo what has already been done.

## Standing Up for Yourself
*Sarah Godwin*
*Smyrna High School, Grade 10*


Ever since I was five years old, I've been teased. I never have been able to stand up for myself, and I still can't. But yesterday on the bus, there was a miracle. This is the one time that I did say something.

On the bus ride home, I was sitting next to some middle school students who were throwing paper balls. I have been hit by a paper ball before, but not ten times in a row. I was sick and tired of this behavior, and I wanted it to stop. When the last paper ball hit me, I yelled, "Ok, that's it! If one more paper ball hits me, I will eradicate a middle schooler! Now, I am sick of this! Stop throwing things at me!" I could not believe what I was saying. Me—who never says anything. I continued, "I am sick and tired of being shy! I am not going to be shy anymore." Wow, where did all that come from?

Then, I noticed that nobody was paying attention to me except one small boy. I was a little bit embarrassed, but then I remembered that they were middle schoolers. Still, I stood up for myself, and boy, did that feel great. Yes, I did it. Did I change the behavior of those middle schoolers—probably not, but hopefully I realized that I can and will be who I am and not allow others to take advantage of me.


## Destination: Dream Place
*Abby Rossi*
*Blackman Elementary School, Grade 5*


Waterfall!
Amazing!
Tremendous!
Exciting!
Radical!
Falling down in joy!
All right!
Loving!
Lolling!

Dreams!
Racing to be there!
Enormous!
Artful!
My favorite place to be!

## Welcome to My Life

*Michael Johnson*
*Smyrna West Alternative School, Grade 8*


Welcome to my life where what you see is what you get.
Does it matter that I started this poem?
Will they listen if I tell 'em?
How can I be sure I won't mess up?
You might think I'm lost, but really I'm helpless.
In a world where I can't tell this.


## Moving Forward

*Emma Sulkowski*
*Siegel High School, Grade 12*


Even simply looking you can see it now,
Standing straighter, speaking confidently, moving outside the norm,
And the list goes on.
The difference between then and now?
CONFIDENCE
But embarking on the road of change was a great challenge,
Walking away from fear, letting go of the words, which I will always remember.
The effect of ridicule and belittling—over and over—
Diminishes self esteem and self confidence.
It IS possible to move on, but the scars,
They take time to heal.
Music, the cause of my self doubt,
Or so I thought,
My rancor for the art I had committed so much energy toward,
I was searching for a new place.
Imagine—six weeks in Northern Michigan,
Surrounded by art and nature.
People coming from all over the world, living together
Bonded by their common passion—the arts
More fun than you could fathom,
Learning to once again love music in its entirety,
Led me to realize that I have many incredible accomplishments,
The scars fading, allowing me to see myself in a new light,
The ultimate destination…
Becoming someone who believes in her abilities and has the confidence to share.

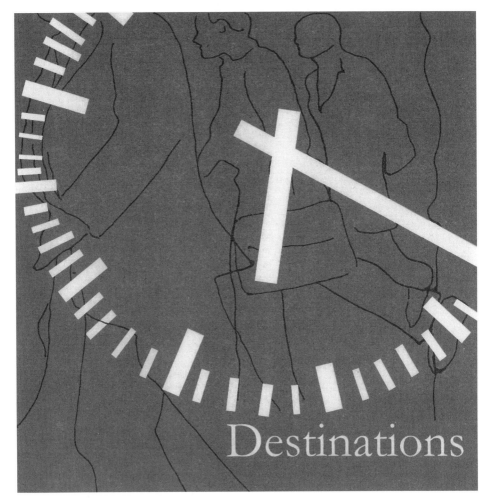

**Where You Want to Go** • *Emily Horn* • *Siegel High School, Grade 11*

# *Acknowledgements*

**Barfield Elementary School**
Sheila Berry
Mary Elizabeth Gillespie
Karen Myers
Lucy Pittenger
Sheralee Riddle
Creeda Wright

**Blackman Elementary School**
Kimberly Christopher
Wendy Davenport
Rachael Fraser
Kelly Henry
Mallory Hinkle
Lynn Kennedy
Julienne Kirin
Kenda Lynch
Kim Marable
Tisonya Mastin
Deborah Maxwell
Ray Ann McCord
Pam Morgan
Amanda Sexton
Michele Slusher
Lorrie Spickard
Wendy Spivey
Cindy Thompson
Felicia Thompson
Laura Tywater
Misty Waddell
Connie Wiel
Mary Wilkerson
April Williams
Ashley Winrow
Fannie Williams
Wanda Williams
Kerri Womack

**Blackman High School**
Ruth Anna Thomason

**Blackman Middle School**
Leisa Barrier
Susan Lewis
Paula Renfroe

**Buchanan Elementary School**
Sarah Raynor
Suzan Warren

**Cedar Grove Elementary School**
Misty Byrd
Kristen Conte
Stacey Harp
Kara Mullican
Connie Phillips
Angela Pope
Stephanie Van Winkle
Dawn Waldron

**Central Middle School**
Anne Marie Gronskei

**Christiana Elementary School**
Christy Brown
Kathleen Davis
Deborah Henderson
Lora Vetter

**Christiana Middle School**
Carol Haislip

**Daniel McKee Alternative School**
Patricia Smith

**David Youree Elementary School**
Angela Montgomery
Melissa Smigielski
Jeania Smith

**Eagleville School**
Beverly Noland Barnes
Melissa Broyles
Theresa Hill
Bill Jarboe
Leslie Trail
Nancy Warden

**Homer Pittard Campus School**
Cindy Cliché
Pam Neal
Kathy Paul
Charlotte Young

**Kittrell Elementary School**
Mary Merrill
Jennifer Smith

**Lascassas Elementary School**
Donna Cowan
Becky Deaton
Jennifer Frazier
Christina Harlan
Melissa Kincaid
Wanda Locker
Katie Lund
Brenda Martin
Bethany Miller
Cindy Nickerson
Kristi Peay
Melanie Rooker

**LaVergne Lake Elementary**
Rachel Baskersville
Aimee Garsnett
Linda Hagan

**LaVergne Middle School**
Patricia Campbell
Jacquelyn McMeen

**McFadden School of Excellence**
Cynthia Davis
Vanessa Tipton

**Oakland High School**
Gina Blackburn
Nancy Jackson

**Riverdale High School**
Patrick White
Renessa Yokley

**Rock Springs Elementary School**
Aimee Garsnett
Jill McHenry
Theresa Moore

**Rock Springs Middle School**
Rhonda Marcum
Jan Wadleigh

**Rockvale Middle School**
Shawn Lee
Ann Patient

**Roy Waldron Elementary School**
Andrea Bontempi
Victoria Duff

**Siegel High School**
Eileen Haynes
Belinda Juergens
Melissa LaDuc
Matt Marlatt
Trish Morgan
Jane Strobel
Barbara Zawislak

**Siegel Middle School**
Teri Beck
Sonya Cox
Susan Royston

**Smyrna High School**
Jean Lemke
Jill Walls
Kelly Wester

**Smyrna Primary School**
Reta Barney
Angeline Hale
Melanie Hatcher
Crystal Keel
Jennifer Monroe
Donna Pierce
Carla Sartin
Boe Washington

**Smyrna West Alternative School**
Lee Farris
Kelly Messerly
Kara Porter
April Sneed

**Stewarts Creek Elementary School**
Trey Duke
Jennifer Johnson

**Stewarts Creek Middle School**
Anna Duncan
Amy Ford
Jane Macomber
Beverly McGee

**Stewartsboro Elementary School**
Patsy Newberry

**Thurman Francis Arts Academy**
Shanya Caldwell
Rosanna Heard
Shannon Marlin

**Walter Hill Elementary School**
Teresa Brockwell
Beverly Carlton
Gina McKee
Dana Palmer

**Wilson Elementary School**
René Davis
Jacci Hooper
Rachel Peay